Reading Essentials and Study Guide

Student Workbook

GLENCOE

World History

Modern Times

 Glencoe

New York, New York   Columbus, Ohio   Chicago, Illinois   Peoria, Illinois   Woodland Hills, California

To the Student

Glencoe World History: Modern Times **Reading Essentials and Study Guide** is designed to help you use recognized reading strategies to improve your reading-for-information skills. For each section of the student textbook, you are alerted to key terms and are asked to draw from prior knowledge, organize your thoughts with a graphic organizer, and then follow a process to read and understand the text. The **Reading Essentials and Study Guide** was prepared to help you get more from your textbook by reading with a purpose.

Using this study tool will also help you learn the California History–Social Science Standards for World History, Culture, and Geography: The Modern World. The standards that apply to a given section are listed on the first page of that section.

Send all inquiries to:
Glencoe/McGraw-Hill
8787 Orion Place
Columbus, OH 43240-4027

ISBN 0-07-872688-3

Printed in the United States of America.

1 2 3 4 5 6 7 8 9 10 047 10 09 08 07 06 05

Table of Contents

California History-Social Science Content Standards for
World History, Culture, and Geography: The Modern World

Chapter 7: East Asia Under Challenge

Chapter 8: War and Revolution

Chapter 9: The West Between the Wars

Chapter 10: Nationalism Around the World

Chapter 11: World War II

Chapter 12: Cold War and Postwar Changes

Chapter 13: The Contemporary Western World

Chapter 14: Latin America

Chapter 15: Africa and the Middle East

Chapter 16: Asia and the Pacific

Chapter 17: Challenges and Hopes for the Future

History-Social Science Standards

The California Grade 10 Content Standards tell you what you need to learn and be able to do as you complete your course in World History, Culture, and Geography: The Modern World. The course is designed to cover important events that have shaped the modern world, from the late 1700s to the present. Reading through these standards with a family member will help you understand the goals for your course–and help you to achieve them.

GRADE TEN

World History, Culture, and Geography: The Modern World

10.1 Students relate the moral and ethical principles in ancient Greek and Roman philosophy, in Judaism, and in Christianity to the development of Western political thought.

10.1.1 Analyze the similarities and differences in Judeo-Christian and Greco-Roman views of law, reason and faith, and duties of the individual.

10.1.2 Trace the development of the Western political ideas of the rule of law and the illegitimacy of tyranny, drawing from the Selections from Plato's *Republic* and Aristotle's *Politics*.

10.1.3 Consider the influence of the U.S. Constitution on political systems in the contemporary world.

10.2 Students compare and contrast the Glorious Revolution of England, the American Revolution, and the French Revolution and their enduring effects worldwide on the political expectations for self-government and individual liberty.

10.2.1 Compare the major ideas of philosophers and their effects on the democratic revolutions in England, the United States, France, and Latin America (e.g., biographies of John Locke, Charles-Louis Montesquieu, Jean-Jacques Rousseau, Simon Bolivar, Thomas Jefferson, James Madison).

10.2.2 List the principles of the Magna Carta, the English Bill of Rights (1689), the American Declaration of Independence (1776), the French Declaration of the Rights of Man and the Citizen (1789), and the U.S. Bill of Rights (1791).

10.2.3 Understand the unique character of the American Revolution, its spread to other parts of the world, and its continuing significance to other nations.

Reading Essentials and Study Guide

Chapter 4, Section 2 *(continued)*

READ TO LEARN

• The Congress of Vienna *(page 265)*

After the defeat of Napoleon, European rulers wanted to restore the old order. The great powers (Great Britain, Austria, Prussia, and Russia) met at the Congress of Vienna in September 1814 to arrange a final peace settlement. The leader of the congress was the Austrian foreign minister, Prince Klemens von Metternich. He claimed that he was guided by the principle of legitimacy. This meant that monarchs from the royal families that had ruled before Napoleon would be restored to their positions of power in order to keep peace and stability in Europe. The great powers rearranged territories in Europe because they believed that this would form a new balance of power. For example, to balance Russian territorial gains, new territories were given to Prussia and Austria.

The arrangements that were worked out at the Congress of Vienna were a victory for rulers who wanted to stop the forces of change begun by the French Revolution. These rulers, like Metternich, believed in the political philosophy known as **conservatism.** Conservatism is based on tradition and social stability. Most conservatives favored obedience to political authority and believed that organized religion was beneficial to order in society. Conservatives hated revolutions and were unwilling to accept demands from people who wanted either individual rights or representative governments.

Academic Vocabulary
stability: the quality, state, or degree of being stable; the strength to stand or endure (p. 265)

To maintain the new balance of power, Great Britain, Russia, Prussia, Austria, and later France, agreed to have meetings that would maintain the peace in Europe. These meetings were called the Concert of Europe. Eventually, most of the great powers adopted a **principle of intervention.** According to this principle, the great powers had the right to send armies into countries where there were revolutions in order to restore legitimate monarchs to their thrones. Britain refused to accept the principle, arguing that the great powers should not interfere in the internal affairs of other states. But the other great powers used military force to crush revolutions in Spain and Italy.

Academic Vocabulary
beneficial: conducive to personal or social well-being (p. 265)

7. What was the principle of intervention?

_____

_____

_____

_____

_____

Reading Essentials and Study Guide

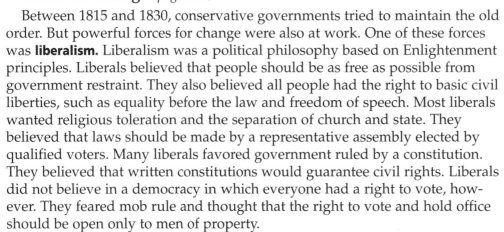

Chapter 4, Section 2 *(continued)*

• Forces of Change *(page 266)*

Between 1815 and 1830, conservative governments tried to maintain the old order. But powerful forces for change were also at work. One of these forces was **liberalism.** Liberalism was a political philosophy based on Enlightenment principles. Liberals believed that people should be as free as possible from government restraint. They also believed all people had the right to basic civil liberties, such as equality before the law and freedom of speech. Most liberals wanted religious toleration and the separation of church and state. They believed that laws should be made by a representative assembly elected by qualified voters. Many liberals favored government ruled by a constitution. They believed that written constitutions would guarantee civil rights. Liberals did not believe in a democracy in which everyone had a right to vote, however. They feared mob rule and thought that the right to vote and hold office should be open only to men of property.

Another force for change was nationalism. Nationalism arose out of people's awareness of being part of a community with common institutions, traditions, language, and customs. This community is called a nation. After the French Revolution, nationalists came to believe that each nationality should have its own government. The Germans were separated into many different states but wanted a single German nation-state with one central government. The Hungarians were part of the Austrian Empire but wanted the right to establish their own government. Conservatives feared these changes and tried hard to repress nationalism, but many liberals supported nationalism. Most liberals believed that freedom would only be possible if people ruled themselves. So most liberals agreed with the nationalists that each people group should have its own state.

Beginning in 1830, liberalism and nationalism began to change the political order in Europe. In France, liberals overthrew the Bourbon king Charles X and established a constitutional monarchy. Louis-Philippe, a cousin of Charles X, became king. Nationalism brought changes in other countries. Belgium rebelled against the Dutch Republic and became an independent state. There were also revolutions in Poland and Italy, but they were soon crushed by the Russians and Austrians.

8. How did conservatives and liberals feel about nationalism in the early nineteenth century?

_____

_____

_____

_____

_____

Reading Essentials and Study Guide

Chapter 4, Section 2 *(continued)*

• The Revolutions of 1848 *(page 268)*

The forces of nationalism and liberalism erupted again in the revolutions of 1848. Beginning in 1846, there were severe economic problems in France. These problems brought suffering to the lower middle class, workers, and peasants. At the same time, the middle class demanded the right to vote, but the government refused to make changes. In 1848, the monarchy was overthrown. A group of republicans set up a provisional or temporary government. The republicans were people who wanted France to be a republic, a government in which leaders are elected. The provisional government called for the election of representatives to a Constituent Assembly that would draw up a new constitution. Election would be by **universal male suffrage,** that is, all adult men could vote. The new constitution was ratified on November 4, 1848. It set up a new republic, called the Second Republic. The Second Republic had a single legislature and a president who served for four years. The legislature and the president were both elected by universal male suffrage. Elections for the presidency were held in December 1848, and Charles Louis Napoleon Bonaparte won. He was the nephew of Napoleon Bonaparte.

News of the 1848 revolution in France led to revolutions in other parts of Europe. Cries for change led many German rulers to promise constitutions, a free press, and jury trials. An all-German parliament, called the Frankfurt Assembly, was held to prepare a constitution for a new united Germany. The members drafted a constitution but had no real way of forcing the German rulers to accept it. As a result, German unification was not achieved.

The Austrian Empire was a **multinational state.** It was a collection of different peoples, including Germans, Czechs, Hungarians, Slovaks, Romanians, Slovenes, Poles, Croats, Serbians, and Italians. Many of these peoples wanted their own governments. In March 1848, there were demonstrations in the major cities in the Austrian Empire. In Vienna, revolutionary forces took control of the capital and demanded a liberal constitution. To appease the revolutionaries, the government gave Hungary its own legislature. In Bohemia, the Czechs demanded their own government. Austrian officials had made concessions to appease the revolutionaries, but they were determined to reestablish control. Austrian military forces crushed the Czech rebels and the rebels in Vienna. In 1849, the Hungarian revolutionaries were also defeated.

In 1848, a revolt also broke out in Lombardy and Venetia, two provinces in Italy that were part of the Austrian Empire. Revolutionaries in other Italian states also took up arms and tried to create liberal constitutions and a unified Italy. By 1849, however, the Austrians had regained complete control over Lombardy and Venetia. Italy was not unified.

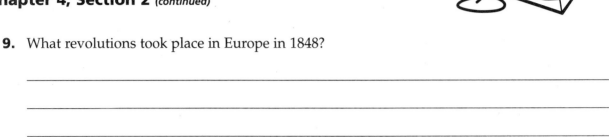

Reading Essentials and Study Guide

Chapter 4, Section 2 *(continued)*

9. What revolutions took place in Europe in 1848?

_____

_____

_____

_____

_____

Reading Essentials and Study Guide

Chapter 4, Section 3

For use with textbook pages 271–279

NATIONAL UNIFICATION AND THE NATIONAL STATE

CONTENT VOCABULARY

militarism reliance on military strength *(page 274)*

kaiser the title of the emperors of the Second German Empire *(page 275)*

plebiscite popular vote on a particular issue *(page 276)*

emancipation setting people free from slavery or serfdom *(page 278)*

abolitionism a movement to end slavery *(page 279)*

secede to withdraw from a political group or nation (used especially for the withdrawal of the Southern States from the Union at the start of the U.S. Civil War) *(page 279)*

DRAWING FROM EXPERIENCE

Have you ever wondered what our country would be like today if the South had won the Civil War? Have you ever thought what it would be like if each state were its own separate country with its own government and national leaders? How would this affect your life?

In the last section, you learned how the forces of liberalism and nationalism led to changes and revolutions in Europe in the first half of the nineteenth century. In this section, you will learn how nationalism contributed to the unification of Germany and Italy. You will also learn how divisions over slavery and other issues threatened national unity in the United States and led to the U.S. Civil War.

> **California History Social Science Standards**
>
> **10.2** Students compare and contrast the Glorious Revolution of England, the American Revolution, and the French Revolution and their enduring effects worldwide on the political expectations for self-government and individual liberty.
>
> **Focuses on:**
> 10.2.5

ORGANIZING YOUR THOUGHTS

Use the chart below to help you take notes. Identify some of the causes and effects of the following wars.

Causes	War	Effects
1.	Crimean War	2.
3.	Franco-Prussian War	4.
5.	United States Civil War	6.

Reading Essentials and Study Guide

Chapter 4, Section 3 *(continued)*

READ TO LEARN

- ## Breakdown of the Concert of Europe *(page 272)*

The revolutions of 1848 had not achieved unification in Germany and Italy. By 1871, however, both Germany and Italy would be unified. The changes that made this possible began with the Crimean War. This war was the result of conflicts between Russia and the Ottoman Empire. The Ottoman Empire had long controlled much of the territory in the Balkans in southeastern Europe. Russia was interested in expanding its territories into the Ottoman lands in the Balkans. In 1853, the Russians invaded the Balkan provinces of Moldavia and Walachia. In response, the Ottoman Turks declared war on Russia. Great Britain and France also declared war on Russia because they were afraid that Russia would gain control of this area. The Crimean War was poorly planned and poorly fought. Heavy losses caused the Russians to seek peace. By the Treaty of Paris in 1856, Russia agreed to allow Moldavia and Walachia to be placed under the protection of all the great powers.

The Crimean War destroyed the Concert of Europe. Austria and Russia became enemies, because Austria had its own interests in the Balkans and had refused to support Russia in the war. Russia withdrew from European affairs for 20 years. Austria was now without friends among the great powers. This new situation opened the door for the unification of Italy and Germany.

7. How did the Crimean War destroy the Concert of Europe?

_____

_____

_____

- ## Italian Unification *(page 273)*

After the failure of the revolution of 1848, people began to look to the northern Italian state of Piedmont for leadership in achieving the unification of Italy. The ruler of the kingdom of Piedmont was King Victor Emmanuel II. The king named Camillo di Cavour his prime minister in 1852. Cavour knew that Piedmont's army was not strong enough to defeat the Austrians. He would need help, so he made an alliance with the French emperor Louis-Napoleon. He then provoked the Austrians into declaring war in 1859. The final result of this conflict was a peace settlement that gave the French Nice and Savoy. (Cavour had promised Nice and Savoy to the French for making the alliance.) Lombardy was given to Piedmont, but Venetia was still controlled by Austria. Cavour's success caused nationalists in some other northern Italian states (Parma, Modena, and Tuscany) to overthrow their governments and join their states to Piedmont.

Reading Essentials and Study Guide

Chapter 4, Section 3 *(continued)*

In southern Italy, Giuseppe Garibaldi, an Italian patriot, raised an army of a thousand volunteers. They were called Red Shirts because of the color of their uniforms. Garibaldi's forces landed in Sicily, which was ruled by France. By the end of July 1860, they controlled most of the island. In August, they crossed over to the mainland and marched up the Italian peninsula. Naples, which was ruled by France, fell in early September. Garibaldi turned over his conquests to Piedmont. On March 17, 1861, a new kingdom of Italy was proclaimed under King Victor Emmanuel II. But the task of Italian unification was not yet complete, because Venetia was still held by Austria and Rome was under the control of the pope.

The Italians gained control of Venetia as a result of the Austro-Prussian War of 1866. The kingdom of Italy was an ally of Prussia in the war. Prussia won the war and gave Venetia to the Italians. In 1870, during the Franco-Prussian War, French troops withdrew from Rome. Their withdrawal made it possible for the Italian army to annex Rome on September 20, 1870. Rome then became the capital of the united Italian state.

8. How did the Austro-Prussian and Franco-Prussian Wars contribute to the unification of Italy?

_____

_____

_____

• German Unification *(page 274)*

After the Frankfurt Assembly was unable to achieve German unification, Germans looked to Prussia to take the lead in this cause. Prussia had become a strong and prosperous state. It was also known for its **militarism** (<u>reliance</u> on military strength). In the 1860s, King William I tried to enlarge the Prussian army. When the Prussian legislature refused to <u>levy</u> new taxes for the army, William I appointed a new prime minister, Count Otto von Bismarck. Bismarck is known for his practice of *realpolitik* ("the politics of reality")— politics based on practical matters rather than on theory or ethics. From 1862 to 1866, he governed Prussia without the approval of the parliament. He collected taxes and strengthened the army. He also followed an active foreign policy that soon led to war. Bismarck created friction with the Austrians and forced them into a war on June 14, 1866. The Austrians were no match for the Prussian army and were defeated on July 3.

Prussia now organized the German states north of the Main River into a North German Confederation. The southern German states were largely Catholic and feared Prussia. But they also feared the French and agreed to sign military alliances with Prussia for protection against the French. In 1870, Prussia and France came into conflict because a relative of the Prussian king

Academic Vocabulary
reliance: the state of being dependant on someone or something (p. 274)

Academic Vocabulary
levy: to impose or collect by legal authority (p. 274)

Reading Essentials and Study Guide

Chapter 4, Section 3 *(continued)*

was a candidate for the throne of Spain. Bismarck took advantage of the mis-understandings between the French and Prussians and pushed the French into declaring war on Prussia on July 19, 1870. This conflict was called the Franco-Prussian War. The French were no match for the Prussian army. The southern German states also joined the war effort against the French. On September 2, 1870, an entire French army and the French ruler, Napoleon III, were captured. France surrendered on January 28, 1871. France had to pay 5 billion franks (about $1 billion) and give up the provinces of Alsace and Lorraine to the new German state.

Even before the war ended, the southern German states had agreed to enter the North German Confederation. On January 18, 1871, William I of Prussia was proclaimed **kaiser** (emperor) of the Second German Empire. German unity had been achieved. With its industrial resources and military might, this new German state became the strongest power on the European continent.

9. How did Prussia achieve German unity?

_____

_____

_____

• Nationalism and Reform in Europe *(page 276)*

In 1832, the British Parliament passed a bill that increased the number of male voters. The new voters were mainly members of the industrial middle class. By giving the industrial middle class an interest in ruling Britain, Britain avoided revolution in 1848. In the 1850s and 1860s, Parliament continued to make social and political reforms that helped the country to remain stable. Another reason for Britain's stability was its continuing economic growth. After 1850, the working classes began to share in the prosperity. Wages for laborers increased more than 25 percent between 1850 and 1870. The British feeling of national pride was well reflected in Queen Victoria. She ruled from 1837 to 1901—the longest reign in English history. Her sense of duty and moral responsibility reflected the attitude of her age, which is known as the Victorian Age.

In France, Louis Napoleon asked the people to restore the empire. In this **plebiscite** (popular vote), 97 percent responded with a yes vote. On December 2, 1852, Louis-Napoleon became Napoleon III, Emperor of France. The Second Empire had begun. The government of Napoleon III was authoritarian. He controlled the armed forces, police, and civil service. Only he could introduce legislation and declare war. There was a Legislative Corps that gave an appearance of representative government, but its members could not initiate legislation or affect the budget. Napoleon III completely controlled the gov-ernment and limited civil liberties. Nonetheless, the first five years of his reign

Reading Essentials and Study Guide

Chapter 4, Section 3 *(continued)*

were a huge success. Railroads, harbors, roads, and canals were built. Iron production tripled. Napoleon III also carried out a vast rebuilding of the city of Paris. In the 1860s, however, oppositions to some of Napoleon's policies grew. In response, Napoleon III gave the legislature more power. In a plebiscite held in 1870, the French people gave Napoleon III another victory. After the French were defeated in the Franco-Prussian War, however, the Second Empire fell.

Until the Austro-Prussian War, the Austrian Empire had been able to keep the ethnic groups in its empire from gaining independence. Austria's defeat in 1866, however, forced the Austrians to make concessions to the Hungarians. The result was the Compromise of 1867. This compromise created the dual monarchy of Austria-Hungary. Austria and Hungary each had its own constitution, its own legislature, its own bureaucracy, and its own capital. The two countries shared a common army, foreign policy, and system of finances. They also had a single monarch. Francis Joseph was both Emperor of Austria and King of Hungary.

At the beginning of the nineteenth century, Russia was overwhelmingly agricultural and autocratic. After the Russians were defeated in the Crimean War. Czar Alexander II decided to make serious reforms. Serfdom was the biggest problem in czarist Russia. On March 3, 1861, Alexander issued an **emancipation** edict that freed the serfs. Peasants could now own property and marry as they chose. The government provided land for the peasants by buying it from the landlords. But there were problems with the new land system. The landowners kept the best lands for themselves, so the Russian peasants did not have enough good land to support themselves. Alexander II attempted other reforms but soon found that he could please no one. He was assassinated in 1881 by a group of radicals. His son and <u>successor</u>, Alexander III, turned against reform and returned to the old methods of repression.

> **Academic Vocabulary**
>
> **successor:** one that follows, especially to a throne, title, estate, or office (p. 278)

10. What was the Compromise of 1867?

_____

_____

_____

• Nationalism in the United States *(page 278)*

In the United States, two factions fought over the division of power in the new government. The Federalists favored a strong central government. The Republicans wanted the federal government to be subordinate to the state governments. These early divisions ended with the War of 1812. There was a surge of national feeling. The election of Andrew Jackson as president in 1828 opened a new era in American politics. Property qualifications for voting had been reduced. The right to vote was extended to all adult white males.

Reading Essentials and Study Guide

Chapter 4, Section 3 *(continued)*

By the mid-nineteenth century, national unity was again an issue. Slavery had become a threat to that unity. The economy in the Southern states was based on growing cotton on plantations, using slave labor. At the same time, **abolitionism,** a movement to end slavery, arose in the North. Abolitionism challenged the Southern way of life. As opinions over slavery grew more divided, compromise became less possible. After Abraham Lincoln was elected president in 1860, a South Carolina convention voted to **secede** (withdraw) from the United States. In February 1861, six more Southern states did the same. A rival nation, the Confederate States of America, was formed. In April, fighting erupted between North and South—the Union and the Confederacy. The American Civil War lasted from 1861 to 1865. It was an extremely bloody war. The Union had more men and resources and gradually wore down the Confederacy. On January 1, 1863, Abraham Lincoln's Emancipation Proclamation declared that most of the nation's slaves were "forever free." The Confederate forces finally surrendered on April 9, 1865. National unity had prevailed in the United States.

11. What was the main issue that divided Federalists and Republicans in the United States before the War of 1812?

_____

_____

_____

Glencoe World History—Modern Times

Name _____ Date _____ Class _____

Reading Essentials and Study Guide

Chapter 4, Section 4

For use with textbook pages 280–285

CULTURE: ROMANTICISM AND REALISM

CONTENT VOCABULARY

romanticism an intellectual movement that emphasized feelings, emotions, and imagination as sources of knowing *(page 281)*

secularization indifference or rejection of religion or religious consideration *(page 284)*

organic evolution the principle that each kind of plant and animal has evolved over a long period of time from earlier and simpler forms of life *(page 284)*

natural selection the process whereby organisms that are more adaptable to the environment survive and thrive, while those that are less adaptable do not survive *(page 284)*

realism a movement in the arts that emphasized a realistic view of the world and focused on the everyday life of ordinary people *(page 284)*

DRAWING FROM EXPERIENCE

Have you ever read the novels *A Christmas Carol, Oliver Twist,* or *Great Expectations,* by Charles Dickens? Perhaps you have seen the movies or plays based on these novels. What is the main theme of these novels?

In the last three sections, you read about the Industrial Revolution and other changes in Europe and North America during the nineteenth century. In this section, you will learn how the Industrial Revolution created a new interest in science, which helped produce the realist movement in the arts. Another movement, romanticism, was also important in the nineteenth century.

> **California History Social Science Standards**
>
> **10.3** Students analyze the effects of the Industrial Revolution in England, France, Germany, Japan, and the United States.
>
> **Focuses on:**
> 10.3.2, 10.3.7

ORGANIZING YOUR THOUGHTS

Use the chart below to help you take notes. Summarize the main emphases and themes of romanticism and realism, and list some of the important writers and artists in these two movements.

Movement	Emphases/Themes	Important Writers	Important Artists
Romanticism	1.	2.	3.
Realism	4.	5.	6.

Reading Essentials and Study Guide

Chapter 4, Section 4 (continued)

READ TO LEARN

• Romanticism *(page 280)*

At the end of the eighteenth century, a new intellectual movement, known as **romanticism,** emerged. It was a reaction to the ideas of the Enlightenment. The Enlightenment had stressed reason as the chief means for discovering truth. The romantics emphasized feelings, emotion, and imagination as ways of knowing. Romantics also valued individualism, the belief in the uniqueness of each person. Many romantics had a strong interest in the past. They revived medieval architecture and built castles, cathedrals, and other public buildings in a style called neo-Gothic. Literature also reflected this interest in the past. For example, many of the novels of Walter Scott were set in medieval England and other historical periods and became best-sellers. The exotic and unfamiliar also attracted many romantics and gave rise to Gothic literature. Mary Shelley's *Frankenstein* and Edgar Allen Poe's short stories are examples of Gothic literature.

The romantics viewed poetry as the direct expression of the soul. Romantic poetry gave expression to one of the most important characteristics of romanticism—its love of nature. This is especially evident in the poetry of William Wordsworth. The worship of nature caused Wordsworth and other romantic poets to be critical of eighteenth-century science. They believed that science had reduced nature to a cold object of study. William Blake was a poet and artist who used the human soul as a source of expressing himself. Like Blake, many romantics were convinced that the emerging industrialization would cause people to become alienated from their inner selves and the natural world around them.

The visual arts and music were also affected by romanticism. Romantic artists <u>abandoned</u> classical reason for warmth and emotion. Romantic art was a reflection of the artist's inner feelings. Eugène Delacroix was one of the most famous romantic painters from France. His paintings showed two chief characteristics: a fascination with the exotic and a passion for color. Romantic trends dominated music during this time. Music historians have called the nineteenth century the age of romanticism. One of the greatest composers of all time, Ludwig van Beethoven, was the bridge between the classical and romantic periods in music. His early work was largely classical, but his music also reflected his deepest inner feelings.

Academic Vocabulary
abandon: to give up control or influence to another person or idea

7. How did many romantics view science and industrialization?

_____

_____

_____

_____

Reading Essentials and Study Guide

Chapter 4, Section 4 *(continued)*

• A New Age of Science *(page 283)*

The Industrial Revolution led to an increased interest in scientific research. By the 1830s, new discoveries in science had brought many practical benefits that affected all Europeans. In biology, Louis Pasteur proposed the germ theory of disease. This was crucial to the development of modern scientific medical practices. In chemistry, Dmitri Mendeleyev classified all the material elements then known on the basis of their atomic weights. In Great Britain, Michael Faraday created a primitive generator that laid the foundation for the use of electric current.

The dramatic material benefits led Europeans to have a growing faith in science. This faith undermined the religious faith of many people. The nineteenth century was an age of increasing **secularization** (indifference or rejection of religion or religious consideration). For many people, truth was now to be found in science and the material existence of humans. Charles Darwin, in particular, created a picture of humans as material beings that were simply part of the natural world. In 1859, Darwin published *On the Origin of Species by Means of Natural Selection*. The basic idea of this book was that each kind of plant and animal had evolved over a long period of time from earlier and simpler forms of life. Darwin called this principle **organic evolution.** Darwin believed that some organisms are more able to <u>adapt</u> to the environment than others, a process that Darwin called **natural selection.** Those <u>variations</u> naturally selected for survival ("survival of the fittest") reproduce and thrive. The unfit do not. In the *Descent of Man*, published in 1871, Darwin argued that human beings had animal origins and were not an exception to the principle of organic evolution. Darwin's ideas created a huge <u>controversy</u>. Some people objected that Darwin's theory made human beings ordinary products of nature rather than unique creatures of God. Others were bothered because they felt he was saying life was a mere struggle for survival. Gradually, however, many scientists and other intellectuals began to accept Darwin's theory.

Academic Vocabulary
adapt: to make fit for a specific or new use or situation by modifying or changing (p. 284)

Academic Vocabulary
variation: difference in the characteristics of an organism from the species or population average (p. 284)

Academic Vocabulary
controversy: a discussion marked by the opposing views of individuals or groups (p. 284)

8. How did achievements in science and technology contribute to secularization in the nineteenth century?

_____

_____

_____

_____

_____

Reading Essentials and Study Guide

Chapter 4, Section 4 (continued)

- **Realism** (page 284)

   Many people believed that the world should be viewed realistically. This belief was closely related to the scientific outlook. **Realism** became a movement in the literary and visual arts. Realists rejected romanticism. Realist writers wanted to write about ordinary people from real life rather than romantic heroes in exotic settings. They also avoided emotional language and used precise description. The realist novel was perfected by the French author Gustave Flaubert. Another important realist was the British novelist Charles Dickens. His novels focused on the lower and middle classes in the Industrial Age.

   Realism also became dominant in art after 1850. Realist artists tried to show the everyday life of ordinary people and nature with photographic realism. The French became leaders in realist painting. Gustave Courbet was the most famous artist of the realist school. One of his famous works, *The Stonebreakers*, shows two roadworkers breaking stones to build a road. To Courbet, no subject was too ordinary, too harsh, or too ugly.

   9. What literary form did realist writers prefer?

   _____

   _____

   _____

   _____

   _____

Reading Essentials and Study Guide

Chapter 5, Section 1

For use with textbook pages 295–300

THE GROWTH OF INDUSTRIAL PROSPERITY

CONTENT VOCABULARY

assembly line a production system with machines and workers arranged so that each person performs an assigned task again and again as the item passes before him or her *(p. 297)*

mass production the production of large quantities of goods using machinery and often an assembly line *(p. 297)*

proletariat the working class *(page 300)*

dictatorship a government in which a person or group has absolute power *(page 300)*

revisionists Marxists who rejected the revolutionary approach and argued that workers must organize in mass political parties and work with other parties to gain reforms *(page 300)*

DRAWING FROM EXPERIENCE

Have you ever thought about ways to improve society? What are some areas of society that need improvement? What are your ideas for improving these areas of society?

In this section, you will learn about the Second Industrial Revolution and the changes that it brought to many European countries. You will also learn how the desire to improve working and living conditions led many industrial workers to form political parties and unions based on the theories of Karl Marx.

> **California History Social Science Standards**
>
> **10.3** Students analyze the effects of the Industrial Revolution in England, France, Germany, Japan, and the United States.
>
> **Focuses on:**
> 10.3.2, 10.3.3, 10.3.4, 10.3.5, 10.3.6

ORGANIZING YOUR THOUGHTS

Use the diagram below to help you take notes. By 1900, Europe was divided into two economic zones. One zone was highly industrialized, and the other was still largely agricultural. Identify the countries or regions that made up each zone.

Economic Zones in Europe (circa 1900)

Industrialized	Agricultural
1.	8.
2.	9.
3.	10.
4.	11.
5.	12.
6.	13.
7.	

Reading Essentials and Study Guide

Chapter 5, Section 1 (continued)

• The Second Industrial Revolution (page 296)

Westerners in the late 1800s had a strong belief in progress. The main reason for this belief was the large number of goals created by the Second Industrial Revolution. The first Industrial Revolution changed the production of textiles, iron, and coal. In the Second Industrial Revolution, new industries arose in steel, chemicals, electricity, and petroleum. The first major change in industry between 1870 and 1914 was the substitution of steel for iron. New methods for shaping steel made it useful in the building of lighter, smaller, and faster machines and engines. It was also used to make railways, ships, and weapons.

Electricity was a major new form of energy. It could be easily converted into other forms of energy, such as heat, light, and motion. In the 1870s, the first practical <u>generators</u> of electrical current were developed. The use of electricity led to a series of inventions. The light bulb was created by Thomas Edison in the United States and Joseph Swan in Great Britain. Alexander Graham Bell invented the telephone in 1876, and Guglielmo Marconi sent the first radio waves across the Atlantic in 1901. Electricity also <u>transformed</u> factories. Conveyor belts, cranes, and machines could all be powered by electricity. With electric lights, factories could remain open 24 hours a day.

Academic Vocabulary
generator: a machine that changes mechanical energy into electrical energy (p. 296)

Academic Vocabulary
transform: to change in composition or structure (p. 296)

The development of the internal combustion engine revolutionized transportation. This engine was powered by oil and gasoline. It made ocean liners, airplanes, and automobiles possible. In 1903, Orville and Wilbur Wright made the first flight in a fixed-wing plane at Kitty Hawk, North Carolina.

Industrial production grew as sales of manufactured goods increased. Europeans could afford to buy more goods for several reasons. Wages for workers increased after 1870. Prices for manufactured goods were lower because of lower transportation costs. The **assembly line** and **mass production** became efficient means of producing goods. In the cities, the first department stores began to sell new products, such as clocks, bicycles, electric lights, and typewriters.

Not all nations benefited from the Second Industrial Revolution. By 1900, Europe was divided into two economic zones. Great Britain, Belgium, France, the Netherlands, Germany, the western part of the Austro-Hungarian Empire, and northern Italy made up an advanced industrialized zone. These nations had a high standard of living and decent transportation systems. Another part of Europe was still primarily agricultural. This was the area to the south and east. It was made up southern Italy, most of Austria-Hungary, Spain, Portugal, the Balkan kingdoms, and Russia. These countries provided food and raw materials for the industrial countries.

The Second Industrial Revolution was a major step toward a true world economy. By 1900, Europeans were receiving beef and wool from Argentina

Reading Essentials and Study Guide

Chapter 5, Section 1 *(continued)*

and Australia, coffee from Brazil, iron ore from Algeria, and sugar from Java. Foreign countries also provided markets for the manufactured goods of Europe. With its capital, industries, and military might, Europe dominated the world economy by the beginning of the twentieth century.

14. How was the Second Industrial Revolution different from the first Industrial Revolution?

_____

_____

_____

_____

_____

• Organizing the Working Classes *(page 299)*

The transition to an industrialized society was very hard on workers. It took many decades for workers to have a higher standard of living. Reformers during this time were opposed to industrial capitalism. Moderate reformers were willing to work within the system for gradual changes. Other, more radical, reformers wanted to abolish the capitalist system entirely. Socialist parties <u>emerged</u> based on the theories of Karl Marx, one of the most influential writers supporting this radical view. In 1848, Marx and Friedrich Engels published *The Communist Manifesto,* in which they blamed the system of industrial capitalism for these poor working conditions. They proposed a new social system. One form of Marxist socialism was eventually called communism. Marx believed that industrialized societies were splitting up into two great classes. One group of people, the oppressors, owned the means of production (land, raw materials, money, and so forth). This gave them the power to control government and society. The other group, the oppressed, depended on the owners of the means of production. The bourgeoisie (the middle class) were the oppressors. The **proletariat** (the working class) were the oppressed. Marx predicted that the struggle between the two groups would finally lead to an open revolution where the proletariat would violently overthrow the bourgeoisie. After their victory, the proletariat would form a **dictatorship** (government in which a person or group has absolute power) to organize the means of production. Marx believed that the final revolution would ultimately produce a classless society.

Academic Vocabulary
emerge: to rise from an obscure or inferior position (p. 299)

In time, working-class leaders formed socialist parties based on Marx's ideas. Most important was the German Social Democratic Party (SPD). Once in parliament, SPD delegates worked to pass laws that would improve conditions for the working class. After the 1912 elections, it became the largest single party in Germany. Socialist parties also emerged in other European countries. In 1889, leaders of the various socialist parties joined together and

Reading Essentials and Study Guide

Chapter 5, Section 1 *(continued)*

formed the Second International. This was an association of national socialist groups that would fight against capitalism worldwide. Marxist parties were divided over their goals. Pure Marxists wanted to overthrow capitalism by a violent revolution. Other Marxists, called **revisionists,** disagreed. They believed that workers must continue to organize in mass political parties and even work with other parties to gain reforms.

Another movement to improve workers' rights focused on the trade union, or labor union. In Great Britain, unions won the right to strike in the 1870s. (A strike is a work stoppage called by members of a union to pressure an employer into meeting their demands.) Workers in factories organized into trade unions so that they could use strikes to achieve reforms. By 1914, trade unions in Europe had made considerable progress in bettering the living and working conditions of the working classes.

15. What was the main difference in the beliefs of pure Marxists and revisionists?

_____

_____

_____

_____

_____

Reading Essentials and Study Guide

Chapter 5, Section 2

For use with textbook pages 301–309

THE EMERGENCE OF MASS SOCIETY

CONTENT VOCABULARY

feminism the movement for women's rights *(page 307)*

literacy the ability to read *(page 308)*

DRAWING FROM EXPERIENCE

Have you ever thought what your life would be like if you were unable to read? What problems would you have? How would this affect your ability to find a job?

In the last section, you read about the Second Industrial Revolution. In this section, you will read about the mass society that emerged as a result of the industrialization of Europe. Public education and an increase in literacy were two products of the new mass society.

California History Social Science Standards

10.3 Students analyze the effects of the Industrial Revolution in England, France, Germany, Japan, and the United States.

Focuses on:

10.3.2, 10.3.3, 10.3.4, 10.3.5, 10.3.6

ORGANIZING YOUR THOUGHTS

Use the pyramid diagram below to help you take notes. List the groups or occupations that made up the elite, the middle classes, and the working classes in Europe at the end of the nineteenth century.

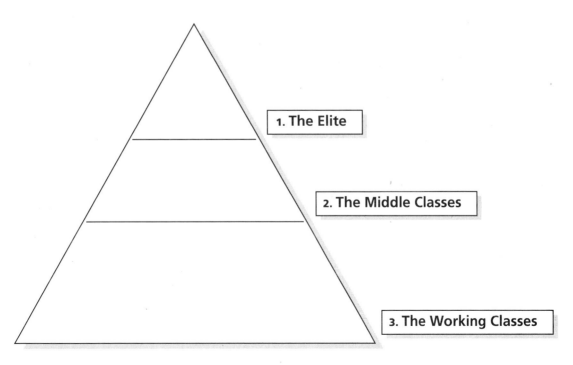

1. The Elite

2. The Middle Classes

3. The Working Classes

Reading Essentials and Study Guide

Chapter 5, Section 2 *(continued)*

READ TO LEARN

• The New Urban Environment *(page 302)*

By the end of the nineteenth century, a mass society emerged in the industrial world. In this society the concerns of the majority—the lower classes—demanded attention. Urban populations grew rapidly because of the vast migration to cities from rural areas. In the cities, people found jobs in factories and, later, in service trades and professions. Cities also grew because of innovations in public health and sanitation. City governments created boards of health to improve the quality of housing. Dwellings were now inspected for health hazards. New building regulations required running water and drainage systems for all new buildings. The ability to bring in clean water and expel sewage was essential to the public health in cities. New systems of aqueducts, tunnels, and pipes made this possible.

> **Academic Vocabulary**
>
> **innovation:** the introduction of a new idea, method, or device (p. 303)

4. What changes were made in cities in the nineteenth century to improve the public health?

_____

_____

_____

_____

_____

• Social Structure of Mass Society *(page 304)*

After 1871, most people enjoyed an improved standard of living. Even so, great poverty remained a part of Western society. The wealthy elite were at the top of European society. This group was only 5 percent of the population but controlled 30 to 40 percent of the wealth. It was made up of the landed aristocrats and the most successful industrialists, bankers, and merchants (the wealthy upper middle class). Members of the elite became leaders in the government and military.

The middle classes consisted of a variety of groups. Below the upper middle class was a group that included lawyers, doctors, members of the civil service, business managers, engineers, architects, accountants, and chemists. Beneath this group was a lower middle class of small shopkeepers, traders, and prosperous peasants. The members of this group provided goods and services for the classes above them. The Second Industrial Revolution produced a new group of white-collar workers between the lower middle class and the lower classes. Although not highly paid, these white-collar workers were often committed to middle-class ideals. A chief objective of middle class life was the belief in hard work. They were also regular churchgoers who believed in Christian morality.

> **Academic Vocabulary**
>
> **objective:** something toward which effort is directed; an aim, goal, or end of action (p. 305)

Reading Essentials and Study Guide

Chapter 5, Section 2 *(continued)*

Below the middle classes were the working classes. They made up almost 80 percent of the European population. Many of the members of these classes were peasants, farm laborers, and sharecroppers. The urban working class consisted of many different groups, including artisans and semi-skilled laborers. At the bottom of the urban working class were the unskilled laborers. They were the largest group of workers and included day laborers and large numbers of domestic servants. Urban workers experienced an improvement in their lives after 1870. Reforms created better living conditions in cities. As wages increased and the cost of consumer goods declined, workers could buy more than just food and housing. Workers now had money for more clothes and even leisure activities. At the same time, strikes were leading to 10-hour workdays and Saturday afternoons off.

5. In what ways did the lives of urban workers improve after 1870?

_____

_____

_____

_____

_____

• **The Experiences of Women** *(page 306)*

During much of the nineteenth century, middle-class and working-class groups believed that women should remain at home and not be allowed in the industrial workforce. Marriage remained the only honorable and available career for most women. One important change in women's lives did occur during this time, however. The number of children born to the average woman began to decline.

Some differences existed in the lives of middle-class and working-class women. Most working-class women had to earn money to help their families. Daughters in working-class families generally worked until they married. After marriage, they often did small jobs at home to help in the raising of younger children. Between 1890 and 1914, however, higher-paying jobs in heavy industry allowed many working-class families to depend on the income of husbands alone.

The Second Industrial Revolution opened the door to new jobs for women. A high demand for relatively low paid white-collar workers led many employers to hire women. Industrial plants and retail shops both needed clerks, typists, secretaries, file clerks, and salespeople. Women also took jobs in the fields of education, health, and social services.

Reading Essentials and Study Guide

Chapter 5, Section 2 (continued)

Modern **feminism,** or the movement for women's rights, had its beginnings during the Enlightenment. In the 1830s, a number of women in the United States and Europe argued for the right of women to divorce and own property. These early efforts were not very successful, and married women in Britain did not win the right to own some property until 1870. The fight for property rights was only the beginning of the women's movement. Some middle-class women fought for and gained access to universities. Others tried to enter occupations dominated by men. Women generally could not train to become doctors. Some, however, entered the medical field by becoming nurses. Amalie Sieveking, Florence Nightingale, and Clara Barton were leaders in the nursing profession.

In the 1840s and 1850s, the movement for women's rights expanded as women demanded equal political rights. Many feminists believed that the right to vote was the key to improving the overall position of women. Suffragists (people who advocate the extension of political rights) had one basic aim: the right of women to full citizenship. Before World War I, however, only women in Norway, Finland, and some states in the United States actually received the right to vote.

6. How did the Second Industrial Revolution open the door to new jobs for women?

_____

_____

_____

_____

_____

_____

• Changes in Education and Leisure (page 308)

Universal education was a result of the mass society of the late nineteenth and early twentieth centuries. Most Western governments began to set up state-financed primary schools. Both boys and girls between the ages of 6 and 12 were required to attend these schools. Western nations made this commitment to public education for two main reasons. One reason was industrialization. The new firms of the Second Industrial Revolution needed trained, skilled labor. Both boys and girls with an elementary education now had new job possibilities. These included white-collar jobs in railways, post offices, and the teaching and nursing fields. A second reason for public education was political. Giving more people the right to vote created a need for better-educated voters. Primary schools also instilled patriotism.

Reading Essentials and Study Guide

Chapter 5, Section 2 (continued)

The most immediate result of public education was in increase in **literacy** (the ability to read). In western and central Europe, most adults could read by 1900. With the increase in literacy after 1870 came the rise of mass newspapers. These newspapers were all written in an easily understood style. They were also sensationalistic, that is, they provided gossip and gruesome details of crimes.

The Second Industrial Revolution allowed people to pursue new forms of leisure. Leisure came to be viewed as what people do for fun after work. The industrial system gave people new times for leisure activities—evening hours, weekends, and a week or two in the summer.

The new forms of leisure tended to be passive, not participatory. Amusement parks introduced people to new experiences and technology. Team sports also developed into another form of leisure. Subways and streetcars made it possible for even the working classes to get to athletic games, amusement parks, and dance halls. Amusement parks and professional sports teams were essentially big businesses organized to make profits.

7. What were the two main reasons that Western nations made a commitment to public education?

_____

_____

_____

_____

_____

_____

Reading Essentials and Study Guide

Chapter 5, Section 3

For use with textbook pages 312–318

THE NATIONAL STATE AND DEMOCRACY

CONTENT VOCABULARY

ministerial responsibility the idea that the prime minister is responsible to the popularly elected legislative body, not to the executive officer *(page 313)*

Duma a legislative assembly in Russia during the time of Nicholas II *(page 315)*

DRAWING FROM EXPERIENCE

Have you ever thought what your life would be like if you had been born in a different country? What do you think would affect you more—the difference in economics or the difference in political systems?

In the last section, you learned about the effects of industrialization in Europe and the United States in the late nineteenth and early twentieth centuries. In this section, you will learn about the political developments during this time. Many nations in Western Europe became more democratic, but rulers in much of Central and Eastern Europe resisted change.

ORGANIZING YOUR THOUGHTS

Use the diagram below to help you take notes. By 1907, Europe was divided into two opposing camps. List the countries in each of the two alliances.

California History Social Science Standards

10.3 Students analyze the effects of the Industrial Revolution in England, France, Germany, Japan, and the United States.
10.4 Students analyze patterns of global change in the era of New Imperialism in at least two of the following regions or countries: Africa, Southeast Asia, China, India, Latin America and the Philippines.
10.5 Students analyze the causes and course of the First World War.

Focuses on:
10.3.2, 10.4.1, 10.5.1

```
              European Alliances
                     1907

              The Triple Alliance

   ┌──────────────┬──────────────┬──────────────┐
   │ 1.           │ 2.           │ 3.           │
   └──────────────┴──────────────┴──────────────┘

              The Triple Entente

   ┌──────────────┬──────────────┬──────────────┐
   │ 4.           │ 5.           │ 6.           │
   └──────────────┴──────────────┴──────────────┘
```

Reading Essentials and Study Guide

Chapter 5, Section 3 *(continued)*

READ TO LEARN

• **Western Europe and Political Democracy** *(page 313)*

By the late nineteenth century, progress had been made toward establishing democracy, especially in Western European nations. In the West, laws were passed that granted universal male suffrage. Also, there was **ministerial responsibility** (the idea that the prime minister is responsible to the popularly elected legislative body, not to the king or president). This principle is <u>crucial</u> for democracy.

By 1871, Great Britain had long had a working two-party parliamentary system. Laws passed in 1867 and 1884 increased the number of adult males who could vote. By the end of World War I, all males over age 21 and women over 30 could vote. The working class supported the Liberal Party, but two developments threatened this support. First, trade unions grew, and they began to favor a more radical change of the economic system. Second, in 1900, a new party, the Labour Party, was formed. It was dedicated to the interest of workers. To keep the support of the workers, the Liberals voted for a series of social reforms. The National Insurance Act of 1911 provided benefits for workers in case of sickness and unemployment. Other laws provided a small pension for people over 70 and <u>compensation</u> for people injured in accidents at work.

In France, the Second Empire had collapsed. It took five years after the Third Republic was set up to proclaim a republican constitution. The new government had a president and a legislature made up of two houses. Members of the upper house, called the Senate, were elected indirectly. Members of the lower house, called the Chamber of Deputies, were elected by universal male suffrage. The powers of the president were not well defined by the constitution. A premier (prime minister) actually led the government. The existence of a dozen political parties forced the premier to depend on a coalition of parties to stay in power. There were frequent changes in government leadership.

By 1870, Italy was a united national state. The nation had little sense of unity, however. A huge gulf separated the poverty-stricken south from the industrialized north. Constant turmoil between labor and industry weakened the nation. Universal male suffrage was granted in 1912 but did little to stop corruption and weakness in the government.

Academic Vocabulary
crucial: important or essential (p. 313)

Academic Vocabulary
compensation: payment to unemployed or injured workers or their dependants (p. 314)

7. What reforms did the Liberal Party make in Great Britain to keep the support of the workers?

_____

_____

_____

_____

Reading Essentials and Study Guide

Chapter 5, Section 3 *(continued)*

- ## Central and Eastern Europe: The Old Order *(page 315)*

Germany became a united state under the leadership of Otto von Bismarck. In 1871 Germany had a two-house legislature. The upper house representatives were appointed by the 26 princely states. The lower house of the German parliament, the Reichstag, was elected by universal male suffrage. Ministers of government were responsible to the emperor, not to the parliament, however. The emperor controlled the armed forces, foreign policy, and the bureaucracy. As chancellor (prime minister), Bismarck did not want Germany to become a democracy. By the reign of William II, emperor from 1888 to 1918, Germany had become the strongest power in Europe. Demands for democracy increased. Conservative forces in Germany tried to block the movement for democracy by supporting a strong foreign policy. They believed that expansion abroad would not only increase profits but also divert people from pursuing democratic reforms.

After the creation of the dual monarchy of Austria-Hungary in 1867, Austria enacted a constitution that, in theory, set up a parliamentary system with ministerial responsibility. In reality, the emperor, Francis Joseph, ignored the system. He appointed and dismissed his own ministers and issued laws when the parliament was not in session. Austria remained troubled by conflicts between the various nationalities in the empire. Representatives of these groups in parliament worked for their freedom. This encouraged the emperor to ignore the parliament even more. On the other hand, Hungary had a parliament that worked. But it was controlled by Magyar landowners who dominated the peasants and ethnic groups.

In Russia, Nicholas II began his rule in 1894 believing that the absolute power of the czars should be preserved. Conditions in Russia were changing, however. Industrialization progressed rapidly in Russia after 1890. With industrialization came an industrial working class, and socialist parties. Government repression forced these parties to go underground. Opposition to the czar finally exploded into the Revolution of 1905. On January 22, a procession of workers went to the Winter Palace in St. Petersburg to present a petition of grievances to the czar. Troops opened fire on the peaceful demonstration, killing hundreds. This "Bloody Sunday" caused workers throughout Russia to call strikes. Nicholas II was forced to grant civil liberties and create a legislative assembly, called the **Duma.** By 1907, however, the czar had already reduced the power of the Duma. He again used the army and bureaucracy to rule.

8. Why did conservative forces in Germany support a strong foreign policy?

_____

_____

_____

Reading Essentials and Study Guide

Chapter 5, Section 3 *(continued)*

- ## The United States *(page 316)*

After the Civil War, the old South was destroyed. One-fifth of the adult male population in the South had been killed, and four million slaves had been freed. In 1865, the Thirteenth Amendment to the Constitution was passed, which abolished slavery. Later, the Fourteenth and Fifteenth Amendments gave citizenship to African Americans and the right to vote to African American males. However, new state laws in southern states soon stripped African Americans of their right to vote.

Between 1860 and 1914, the United States shifted from an agrarian to an industrial nation. Industrialization led to urbanization. By 1900, over 40 percent of Americans lived in cities. Europeans migrated to the United States in massive numbers. The United States had become the world's richest nation, but serious problems remained. In 1890, the richest 9 percent of Americans owned 71 percent of the wealth. Labor unrest led workers to try to organize unions, but the American Federation of Labor represented only 8.4 percent of the labor force.

From the mid-nineteenth century, the United States began to expand abroad. The Samoan Islands in the Pacific became the first important United States colony. As more Americans settled in Hawaii, they sought to gain political power. In 1893, American residents, aided by U.S. Marines from the ship U.S.S. *Boston*, overthrew the monarchy of Queen Liliuokalani (lee•lee•oo•oh•kah•LAH•nee). Five years later, the United States formally annexed Hawaii. In the same year, the United States defeated Spain in the Spanish-American War. As a result, the United States acquired Puerto Rico, Guam, and the Philippines. By the beginning of the twentieth century, the United States had an empire.

9. What land did the United States acquire in the late nineteenth century?

_____

_____

_____

_____

Reading Essentials and Study Guide

Chapter 5, Section 3 *(continued)*

- ## International Rivalries *(page 317)*

    Otto von Bismarck was afraid that France would create an anti-German alliance, so he created an alliance with Austria-Hungary in 1879. In 1882, Italy joined the alliance. The Triple Alliance of 1882 united Germany, Austria-Hungary, and Italy in a defensive alliance against France. At the same time, Bismarck had a separate treaty with Russia and tried to remain on good terms with Great Britain. In 1890, Emperor William II fired Bismarck and took control of Germany's foreign policy. He dropped the treaty with Russia. This brought France and Russia together. In 1894, they formed a military alliance. Over the next 10 years, German policies caused the British to draw closer to France. By 1907, an alliance of Great Britain, France, and Russia—known as the Triple Entente—was formed. Europe was now divided into two opposing camps that became more and more unwilling to compromise. A series of crises in the Balkans between 1908 and 1913 set the stage for World War I.

10. What sequence of events led to the formation of the Triple Entente?

_____

_____

_____

_____

_____

- ## Crises in the Balkans *(page 317)*

    During the nineteenth century, the Balkan provinces had gradually gained their freedom. By 1878, Greece, Serbia, Romania, and Montenegro had become independent states. Bulgaria did not become totally independent, but was allowed to operate under Russian protection. The Balkan territories of Bosnia and Herzegovina were placed under the protection of Austria-Hungary. In 1908, Austria-Hungary annexed Bosnia and Herzegovina. Serbia was outraged. Bosnia and Herzegovina were Slavic-speaking territories, and Serbia had hopes of creating a large Serbian kingdom that would include most of the southern Slavs. Backed by the Russians, the Serbs prepared for war against Austria-Hungary. Emperor William II of Germany demanded that the Russians accept Austria-Hungary's annexation of Bosnia and Herzegovina or face war with Germany. The Russians backed down, but two wars between Balkan states in 1912 and 1913 created more tensions between the great powers.

Reading Essentials and Study Guide

Chapter 5, Section 3 (continued)

The Serbians blamed Austria-Hungary for their failure to create a large Serbian kingdom. Austria-Hungary was convinced that Serbia was a threat to its empire and must be crushed. As Serbia's chief supporters, the Russians were angry and determined not to back down again. The allies of Austria-Hungary and Russia were determined to support their allies more strongly in another crisis. By the beginning of 1914, most of the countries of Europe viewed each other with suspicion.

11. What tensions existed in Europe at the beginning of 1914?

_____

_____

_____

_____

_____

Reading Essentials and Study Guide

Chapter 5, Section 4

For use with textbook pages 319–325

TOWARD THE MODERN CONSCIOUSNESS

CONTENT VOCABULARY

psychoanalysis a method of psychotherapy developed by Freud, in which a therapist and patient probe deeply into a patient's memory *(page 321)*

pogrom an organized massacre (especially of Jews) *(page 323)*

modernism changes in the arts in the late nineteenth and early twentieth centuries involving a break with traditional literary and artistic styles and a search for new forms of expression *(page 323)*

DRAWING FROM EXPERIENCE

Do you like modern art? Who is your favorite artist? Is there a particular movement that you are especially interested in?

In the last three sections, you read about the Second Industrial Revolution and other social and political changes in the late 1800s and early 1900s. In this section, you will read about new ideas in the arts and sciences during this time.

ORGANIZING YOUR THOUGHTS

Use the diagram below to help you take notes. In the late 1800s and early 1900s, many writers and artists rebelled against traditional literary and artistic styles. List the movements in literature, painting, architecture, and music during this period. Also list some of the important writers, artists, and musicians in these movements.

California History Social Science Standards

10.3 Students analyze the effects of the Industrial Revolution in England, France, Germany, Japan, and the United States.
10.4 Students analyze patterns of global change in the era of New Imperialism in at least two of the following regions or countries: Africa, Southeast Asia, China, India, Latin America and the Philippines.

Focuses on:
10.3.2, 10.4.1

```
                          Modernism
   ┌──────────────┬────────────┴─────────────┬──────────────┐
1. Literature   2. Painting          3. Architecture      4. Music
```

Reading Essentials and Study Guide

Chapter 5, Section 4 *(continued)*

READ TO LEARN

- **From Certainty to Uncertainty** *(page 320)*

   In the nineteenth century, Westerners had a view of the world that was based on the ideas of Isaac Newton. The universe was viewed as a giant machine. Matter was thought to be composed of solid material bodies called atoms. Time, space, and matter were believed to be objective realities that existed independently of people observing them. These views were questioned at the end of the nineteenth century. The French scientist Marie Curie discovered that an element called radium gave off energy, or radiation, that came from the atom itself. This meant that atoms were not simply hard material bodies but were small, active worlds.

   At the beginning of the twentieth century, a new view of the universe was provided by Albert Einstein. In 1905, Einstein published his special theory of relativity. It stated that space and time are not absolute but are relative to the people observing them. Matter and energy also reflect the relativity of time and space. Einstein concluded that matter is simply another form of energy. This idea led to an understanding of the vast energies contained within the atom and to the Atomic Age. To some people, however, a relative universe was a universe without certainty.

   The ideas of Sigmund Freud added to the uncertainty that people felt about the world at the turn of the century. In 1900 his theories were published in *The Interpretation of Dreams*. According to Freud, human behavior was strongly determined by past experiences. Freud believed that painful experiences were repressed, or hidden, from a person's conscious awareness. But these experiences continued to influence behavior. Repression of these experiences began in childhood. Freud devised a method by which a therapist and patient could probe deeply into the patient's memory. This method is called **psychoanalysis.** Freud's ideas gained worldwide acceptance in the 1920s. Psychoanalysis developed into a major profession. Freudian terms, such as *unconscious* and *repression,* became standard vocabulary words.

5. How did Einstein's theory of relativity change people's view of the universe?

_____

_____

_____

_____

_____

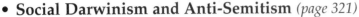

Reading Essentials and Study Guide

Chapter 5, Section 4 *(continued)*

- ## Social Darwinism and Anti-Semitism *(page 321)*

In the late nineteenth and early twentieth centuries, scientific theories were sometimes applied inappropriately. For example, nationalists and racists applied the theories of Charles Darwin to human society. Their ideas are known as Social Darwinism. One Social Darwinist, Herbert Spencer, argued that social progress came from the "struggle for survival" in which the "fit" survive. Some businessmen used Social Darwinism to explain their success. They believed that they were successful because they were "fit" (strong and capable). Extreme nationalists also believed that nations were engaged in a "struggle for existence" in which only the fittest (the strongest) survived. In Germany, extreme nationalism and racism were combined. Houston Stewart Chamberlain, for example, believed that Germans were the only pure successors of the Aryans (who were the original creators of Western culture, according to Chamberlain). Chamberlain also believed that Jews were enemies who wanted to destroy the Aryan race.

Anti-Semitism (hostility toward and <u>discrimination</u> against Jews) had been a part of European civilization since the Middle Ages. In the nineteenth century, Jews were granted legal equality in many European countries. Many Jews became successful as bankers, lawyers, scientists, scholars, and journalists. Discrimination still existed, however. In 1894, Alfred Dreyfus, a French Jew, was found guilty of selling army secrets and was condemned to life imprisonment. Evidence soon showed that Dreyfus was innocent and that the real traitor was a Catholic aristocrat. But the army refused a new trial. Public outrage finally forced the government to pardon Dreyfus in 1899.

In Germany and Austria-Hungary, new parties arose during the 1880s and 1890s that used anti-Semitism to win votes. The worst treatment of Jews at the turn of the century occurred in eastern Europe, where a majority of the world's Jews lived. Russian Jews were forced to live in certain regions of the country. Persecutions and **pogroms** (organized massacres) were widespread. Hundreds of thousands of Jews decided to emigrate (move to another country) to escape the persecution. Many went to the United States. Some went to Palestine, the land of ancient Israel. Palestine became home for a Jewish nationalist movement called Zionism. Settlement in Palestine was difficult because it was part of the Ottoman Empire and the Ottomans opposed Jewish immigration. Even so, about 3,000 Jews went <u>annually</u> to Palestine between 1904 and 1914.

Academic Vocabulary
discrimination: prejudice, usually based on race, religion, class, sex, or age (pp. 322, 725)

Academic Vocabulary
annual: occurring or happening every year or once a year; yearly (p. 323)

Reading Essentials and Study Guide

Chapter 5, Section 4 *(continued)*

6. Why did so many Jews decide to emigrate around the turn of the century?

_____

_____

_____

_____

_____

• The Culture of Modernity *(page 323)*

Between 1870 and 1914, many writers and artists rebelled against traditional literary and artistic styles. The changes that they produced have since been called **modernism.** During much of the nineteenth century, literature was dominated by naturalism. Naturalists felt that literature should be realistic and address social problems. Two examples of naturalist writers are Henrik Ibsen and Émile Zola. At the beginning of the twentieth century, a group of writers known as symbolists caused a literary revolution. They were primarily interested in writing poetry and were influenced by the ideas of Freud. They believed that the external world was only a collection of symbols that reflected the true reality—the human mind.

The period from 1870 to 1914 was one of the most productive in the history of the visual arts. Impressionism was a movement that began in France in the 1870s. Impressionist artists rejected studios and went out into the countryside to paint nature directly. One important Impressionist was Claude Monet. In his paintings, he tried to capture the interplay of light, water, and sky. Other Impressionist painters include Pierre-Auguste Renoir and Berthe Morisot. In the 1880s, a new movement, known as Postimpressionism, arose in France. Vincent van Gogh is one famous Postimpressionist. For van Gogh, art was a spiritual experience. He believed that artists should paint what they feel.

Realism in painting began to decline. The spread of photography was one important reason. Now, anyone could take a photograph that looked exactly like the subject. Artists began to realize that their strength was not in mirroring reality, but in creating reality. Between 1905 and 1914, artists searched for individual expression. This search created modern art. One of the most important figures in modern art was Pablo Picasso. He painted in many different styles. He also created a new style, called cubism, that used geometric designs to recreate reality in the viewer's mind. In 1910, abstract painting began. Wassily Kandinsky was one of the founders of abstract expressionism. He tried to avoid visual reality completely. He believed that art should speak directly to the soul and should use only line and color.

Modernism in the arts revolutionized architecture. A new movement in architecture, known as functionalism, developed. Functionalism said

Reading Essentials and Study Guide

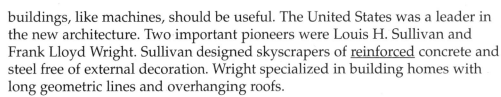

Chapter 5, Section 4 *(continued)*

buildings, like machines, should be useful. The United States was a leader in the new architecture. Two important pioneers were Louis H. Sullivan and Frank Lloyd Wright. Sullivan designed skyscrapers of <u>reinforced</u> concrete and steel free of external decoration. Wright specialized in building homes with long geometric lines and overhanging roofs.

> **Academic Vocabulary**
>
> **reinforce:** to strengthen by additional assistance, material, or support; make stronger (p. 325)

At the beginning of the twentieth century, developments in music paralleled developments in painting. The music of the Russian composer Igor Stravinsky was the first to reflect expressionist theories. His ballet *The Rite of Spring* revolutionized the world of music.

7. How did photography contribute to the decline of realism in painting?

_____

_____

_____

_____

_____

Reading Essentials and Study Guide

Chapter 6, Section 1

For use with textbook pages 335–341

COLONIAL RULE IN SOUTHEAST ASIA

CONTENT VOCABULARY

New Imperialism imperialism of the late nineteenth century during which Europeans sought nothing less than direct control over vast territories, mainly in Africa *(page 336)*

protectorate a political unit that depends on another government for its protection *(page 338)*

indirect rule a system of colonial government in which local rulers were allowed to maintain their positions of authority and status *(page 339)*

direct rule a system of colonial government in which local rulers were removed from power and replaced with a new set of officials brought from the mother country *(page 339)*

DRAWING FROM EXPERIENCE

Do you think there are any good reasons for one country to take control of another country? If so, under what circumstances do you think it would be justified? If not, why not?

In this section, you will learn about the "New Imperialism" of the late nineteenth century. European nations began to acquire colonies in order to obtain raw materials and markets for their manufactured goods.

> **California History
> Social Science Standards**
>
> **10.4** Students analyze patterns of global change in the era of New Imperialism in at least two of the following regions or countries: Africa, Southeast Asia, China, India, Latin America and the Philippines.

ORGANIZING YOUR THOUGHTS

Use the chart below to help you take notes. Indicate which Western power (France, Great Britain, Holland, or the United States,) controlled each of the following countries in Southeast Asia at the end of the nineteenth century. (If a country remained free of colonial rule, write "none.")

Southeast Asian Country	Controlling Country:
Burma	1.
Cambodia	2.
East Indies	3.
Laos	4.
Philippines	5.
Singapore	6.
Thailand	7.
Vietnam	8.

Reading Essentials and Study Guide

Chapter 6, Section 1 *(continued)*

READ TO LEARN

• The New Imperialism *(page 336)*

In the nineteenth century, a new phase of Western expansion into Asia and Africa began. Beginning in the 1880s, European nations began to compete for overseas territory. Imperialism, (the extension of a nation's power over other lands) was not new. But the **"New Imperialism"** of the late nineteenth century was different. Previously, European expansion in Africa and Asia had been limited to setting up a few trading posts. Now European nations wanted direct control over vast territories.

Europeans had various motives for imperialism. There was a strong economic motive. Europeans were looking for raw materials, such as rubber, oil, and tin, for their industries. They were also looking for new markets for their manufactured goods. They wanted more direct control over the areas with the raw materials and markets. There were also political motives. European nations were rivals. They tried to acquire colonies in order to gain an advantage over their rivals. Some people believed that a nation could not be great without colonies. Imperialism was also tied to Social Darwinism and racism. Racism is the belief that race determines traits and capabilities. Racists believe that particular races are superior or inferior to others. Finally, some Europeans had religious and humanitarian motives. They believed that Europeans had a moral responsibility to civilize primitive people. They called this responsibility "the white man's burden." These people believed that Western nations should help the nations of Asia and Africa. To some, this meant bringing the Christian message to these nations. To others, it meant bringing the benefits of Western capitalism and democracy to these countries.

9. How was the "New Imperialism" different from earlier expansion by European nations?

_____

_____

_____

_____

• Colonial Takeover in Southeast Asia *(page 337)*

By 1900, nearly all of Southeast Asia was under Western rule. In 1819, Britain founded a new British colony on a small island at the tip of the Malay Peninsula called Singapore. Singapore soon became a major stopping point for steamships going to or from China. The next country to fall to the British was the kingdom of Burma. Britain wanted control of Burma in order to protect its possessions in India. It also wanted a land route through Burma into South China.

Reading Essentials and Study Guide

Chapter 6, Section 1 (continued)

The French watched nervously as the British moved into Burma. France had missionaries in Vietnam. To keep the British from moving into Vietnam, the French government decided to force the Vietnamese to accept French protection. The Vietnamese ruler gave up territories in the Mekong River delta. The French also occupied the city of Saigon. During the next 30 years, the French extended their control over the rest of the country. In 1884, France seized the city of Hanoi and later made the Vietnamese Empire a French **protectorate** (a political unit that depends on another government for its protection). In the 1880s, France also extended its control over Cambodia, Annam, Tonkin, and Laos. By 1887, France included all of its new possessions in a new Union of French Indochina.

After the French conquest of Indochina, Thailand (then called Siam) was the only remaining free state in Southeast Asia. Two remarkable rulers, King Mongkut and his son King Chulalongkorn, were able to prevent the French and British from placing Thailand under colonial rule. Both kings promoted Western learning and had friendly relations with major European powers. In 1896, Britain and France agreed to maintain Thailand as an independent buffer state between their possessions in Southeast Asia.

One more conquest took place in Southeast Asia at the end of the nineteenth century. In 1898, during the Spanish-American War, United States naval forces under Commodore George Dewey defeated the Spanish fleet in Manila Bay in the Philippines. President William McKinley decided to turn the Philippines into an American colony. The Philippine Islands gave the United States a convenient jumping-off point for trade with China. Many Americans, including President McKinley, also believed that Western nations had a moral obligation to "civilize" other parts of the world. The Filipinos did not agree. Emilio Aguinaldo was the leader of a movement for independence in the Philippines. His guerrilla forces fought against U.S. troops to gain their independence, but they were defeated.

10. How was Thailand able to remain free of colonial rule?

_____

_____

_____

_____

• Colonial Regimes in Southeast Asia (page 339)

Western powers ruled their new colonial empires either by indirect or direct rule. Their goals were to <u>exploit</u> natural resources and open up markets for their manufactured goods. Sometimes a colonial power could accomplish its goals through cooperation with local rulers or political elites. In these cases, **indirect rule** was used. Local rulers were allowed to maintain their positions of

Academic Vocabulary
exploit: to make productive use of, sometimes selfishly or unjustly (p. 339)

Reading Essentials and Study Guide

Chapter 6, Section 1 (continued)

authority and status. Indirect rule made it easier to gain access to an area's natural resources. It also lowered the cost of government, because fewer officials had to be trained. Indirect rule also had less impact on local culture. One example of indirect rule was in the Dutch East Indies. Officials of the company allowed local landed aristocrats in the Dutch East Indies to control local government. These local elites maintained order and collected taxes.

Indirect rule was not always possible, however. This was especially true when local rulers resisted colonial rule. In these cases, the local rulers were removed from power and replaced with a new set of officials brought from the mother country. This system is called **direct rule.** In Burma, for example, the monarchy opposed colonial rule. As a result, Great Britain abolished the monarchy and ruled the country directly through its colonial government in India.

In Indochina, France used both direct and indirect rule. It <u>imposed</u> direct rule on the southern provinces in the Mekong delta, but the northern parts of Vietnam were governed as a protectorate. The emperor still ruled but had little power. France had a similar policy in Cambodia and Laos. Local rulers were left in charge, with French advisors to counsel them.

> **Academic Vocabulary**
>
> **impose:** to establish or bring about as if by force (p. 339)

To justify their conquests, Western nations had said they wanted to bring the blessings of Western civilization to their colonies. Many colonial powers said they wanted to teach the native peoples about the democratic process. However, many Westerners became afraid of giving native peoples political rights. They were afraid that the native peoples would want full participation in the government or even independence.

The colonial powers did not want their colonies to develop their own industries. Colonial policy stressed the export of raw materials. In many cases, this policy led to some form of plantation agriculture, in which peasants worked as wage laborers on plantations owned by foreigners. Plantation owners kept the wages at poverty levels in order to increase the owners' profits. Conditions on plantations were often so unhealthy that thousands died. Taxes were also a burden for peasants. But colonial rule did bring some benefits to Southeast Asia. Colonial governments built railroads and highways. In some countries, small growers of rubber, palm oil, coffee, tea, and spices were able to benefit from the development of an export market.

11. How are direct and indirect rule different? Why was indirect rule not always used?

_____

_____

_____

_____

Reading Essentials and Study Guide

Chapter 6, Section 1 *(continued)*

- ## Resistance to Colonial Rule *(page 340)*

Many people in Southeast Asia were very unhappy about being ruled by Western powers. At first, resistance came from the ruling classes. In Burma, for example, the monarch himself fought against British rule. Sometimes, resistance to Western rule took the form of peasant revolts. Many peasants were driven off the land to make way for plantations. This led to peasant uprisings against the British colonial <u>regime</u>. Early resistance movements failed, but a new kind of resistance began to emerge at the beginning of the twentieth century. This resistance was based on nationalism. The leaders were often part of a new class that had been created by colonial rule—westernized intellectuals in the cities. This new class had been educated in Western-style schools. They were the first generation of Asians to understand the institutions and values of the West. Many spoke Western languages. At first, many of the leaders of these movements did not focus on the idea of nationhood. They simply tried to defend the economic interests or religious beliefs of the natives. In Burma, for example, students at the University of Rangoon formed an organization to protest British lack of respect for local religious traditions. Not until the 1930s did these resistance movements begin to demand national independence.

> | Academic Vocabulary |
> | --- |
> | **regime:** a government in power (p. 341) |

12. What new form of resistance to colonial rule began to emerge at the beginning of the twentieth century?

_____

_____

_____

_____

Reading Essentials and Study Guide

Chapter 6, Section 2

For use with textbook pages 342–349

EMPIRE BUILDING IN AFRICA

CONTENT VOCABULARY
annex to incorporate a country within a state *(page 343)*
indigenous native to a region *(page 347)*

DRAWING FROM EXPERIENCE

Has anyone ever told you that your traditions and customs were wrong? How would this make you feel?

In the last section, you read about imperialism in Southeast Asia. In this section, you will learn about imperialism in Africa. Most colonial powers did not respect the local customs and traditions of the countries they controlled.

ORGANIZING YOUR THOUGHTS

Use the chart below to help you take notes. List which European nations had claims in the following parts of Africa by 1914.

California History Social Science Standards

10.3 Students analyze the effects of the Industrial Revolution in England, France, Germany, Japan, and the United States.
10.4 Students analyze patterns of global change in the era of New Imperialism in at least two of the following regions or countries: Africa, Southeast Asia, China, India, Latin America and the Philippines.
Focuses on:
10.3.4

African Region	European Nations With Claims in the Region
West Africa	**1.**
North Africa	**2.**
Central Africa	**3.**
East Africa	**4.**
South Africa	**5.**

Reading Essentials and Study Guide

Chapter 6, Section 2 (continued)

READ TO LEARN

• West Africa (page 343)

Between 1880 and 1900, European countries took control of nearly all of Africa. West Africa had been particularly affected by the slave trade, but that had begun to decline by 1800. By the 1890s, slavery had been abolished in all major countries of the world. As slavery declined, Europe became interested in other forms of trade. Europeans sold textiles and other manufactured goods in exchange for peanuts, timber, hides, and palm oil from West Africa. Early in the nineteenth century, the British set up settlements along the Gold Coast and in Sierra Leone.

For a long time, most African nations were able to maintain their independence. However, in 1874, Great Britain **annexed** (incorporate a country within a state) the west coastal states. They called this first British colony Gold Coast. At about the same time, Britain established a protectorate over warring groups in Nigeria. By 1900, France had added the huge area of French West Africa to its colonial empire, and Germany controlled Togo, Cameroon, German Southwest Africa, and German East Africa.

6. What forms of trade replaced the slave trade in West Africa?

_____

_____

_____

_____

• North Africa (page 343)

Egypt had been part of the Ottoman Empire, but Egyptians began to seek their independence as the Ottoman Empire declined. In 1805, an officer of the Ottoman army named Muhammad Ali seized power and established a separate Egyptian state. During the next 30 years, he introduced reforms to bring Egypt into the modern world.

Europeans were interested in Egypt because they wanted to build a canal east of Cairo to connect the Mediterranean and Red Seas. The Suez Canal was completed in 1869. The British were especially interested in the canal. They believed it was their "lifeline to India." In 1875, Britain bought Egypt's share in the Suez Canal. When an Egyptian army revolt against foreigners broke out in 1881, Britain suppressed the revolt. Egypt became a British protectorate in 1914. The British believed they should also control the Sudan, south of Egypt, in order to protect both Egypt and the Suez Canal. But Muslim troops under Muhammad Ahmad resisted. Not until 1898 were British troops able to seize the Sudan.

Reading Essentials and Study Guide

Chapter 6, Section 2 *(continued)*

The French also had colonies in North Africa. In 1879, the French government took control of Algeria. Two years later, France imposed a protectorate on Tunisia. In 1912, France also established a protectorate over much of Morocco. In 1911, Italy invaded and seized Turkish Tripoli, which it renamed Libya.

7. Why was Egypt important to Europeans in the nineteenth century?

_____

_____

_____

_____

_____

• **Central Africa** *(page 345)*

Explorers, such as David Livingstone, aroused Europeans' interest in the jungles of Central Africa. Livingstone arrived in 1841. For 30 years, he explored Central Africa. After Livingstone's death in 1873, Henry Stanley carried on the work of exploration. In the 1870s, Stanley explored the Congo River and sailed down it to the Atlantic Ocean. He encouraged the British to send settlers to the Congo River basin. When Britain refused, he turned to King Leopold II of Belgium. King Leopold became the real driving force behind the colonization of Central Africa. In 1876, he hired Stanley to set up Belgian settlements in the Congo. Belgium ended up with the territories around the Congo River. France occupied the areas farther north.

8. How did Europeans become interested in Central Africa?

_____

_____

_____

_____

• **East Africa** *(page 346)*

By 1885, Britain and Germany had become the chief rivals in East Africa. At first, the German chancellor Otto von Bismarck did not think that colonies were very important. But more and more Germans wanted an empire, so Bismarck became interested in colonialism for political reasons. Germany had possessions in West Africa, but it began to seek colonies in East Africa. The British were also interested in East Africa, because control of East Africa

Reading Essentials and Study Guide

Chapter 6, Section 2 *(continued)*

would connect the British Empire in Africa from Egypt in the north to South Africa. Portugal and Belgium also claimed parts of East Africa. To settle these <u>conflicting</u> claims, the Berlin Conference met in 1884 and 1885. The conference officially recognized both British and German claims in East Africa. Portugal received a clear claim on Mozambique. No Africans were present at this conference.

> **Academic Vocabulary**
>
> **conflict:** struggle resulting from opposing needs, drives, wishes, or external or internal demands (p. 346)

9. What was the purpose of the Berlin Conference?

_____

_____

_____

_____

_____

- **South Africa** *(page 347)*

By 1865, the total white population in South Africa had risen to nearly 200,000. The descendants of the original Dutch settlers were called Boers or Afrikaners. They had occupied Cape Town and surrounding areas in South Africa since the 1600s. During the Napoleonic Wars, the British seized these lands from the Dutch. Afterward, the British encouraged settlers to come to this area, which they called Cape Colony. In the 1830s, the Boers fled northward to the region between the Orange and Vaal Rivers and to the region north of the Vaal River. In these areas, the Boers formed two independent republics—the Orange Free State and the Transvaal (later called the South African Republic). The Boers believed that God ordained white superiority. They put many of the **indigenous** (native to a region) peoples in these areas on reservations. The Boers had frequent battles with the indigenous Zulu people. In the late 1800s, the British became involved in conflicts with the Zulu, and the Zulu were defeated.

In the 1880s, Cecil Rhodes, the prime minister of Cape Colony, influenced British policy in South Africa. Rhodes had started diamond and gold companies that made him a fortune. He gained control of a territory north of the Transvaal, which he named Rhodesia after himself. In 1896, the British government forced him to resign as prime minister of Cape Colony after it was discovered that he planned to overthrow the Boer government of the South African Republic. This was too late to avoid a war between the British and the Boers, however. This war was called the Boer War and lasted from 1899 to 1902. Boer women and children were put in detention camps, where as many as 20,000 died. Eventually, the British army won the war. In 1910, the British created an independent Union of South Africa. This new nation combined the

Reading Essentials and Study Guide

Chapter 6, Section 2 (continued)

old Cape Colony and the Boer republics. To appease the Boers, the British agreed that only whites and a few property-holding Africans could vote.

10. Who were the Boers?

_____

_____

_____

_____

_____

• **Colonial Rule in Africa** (page 348)

By 1914, Great Britain, France, Germany, Belgium, Italy, Spain, and Portugal had divided up Africa. Only Liberia and Ethiopia remained free states. Native peoples who tried to resist were no match for the superior military power of the Europeans. The British used indirect rule in their territories in Africa. In some areas, the British simply asked a local ruler to accept British authority and to fly the British flag over official buildings. The system of indirect rule had one good feature: it did not disrupt local customs and institutions. However, it did have some unfortunate <u>consequences</u>. The system was basically a fraud because British administrators made all major decisions. Another problem was that indirect rule kept the old African elites in power. In this way, it sowed the seeds for class and tribal tensions.

Most other European nations used a form of direct rule. This was true in the French colonies. At the top was a French official, usually known as a governor-general. He ruled with the help of a bureaucracy in the capital city of the colony. The French believed in assimilating Africans into French culture rather than preserving native traditions. Africans were eligible to run for office and even to serve in the French National Assembly in Paris. A few were appointed to high positions in the colonial administration.

Academic Vocabulary
consequence: something produced by a cause or unavoidably following from a set of conditions (p. 348)

11. What were the good and bad features of indirect rule?

_____

_____

_____

_____

_____

Reading Essentials and Study Guide

Chapter 6, Section 2 *(continued)*

- ## Rise of African Nationalism *(page 349)*

A new class of leaders emerged in Africa by the beginning of the twentieth century. They were educated in colonial schools or in Western nations. The members of this new class admired Western civilization and sometimes disliked the ways of their own countries. Many resented foreigners and their lack of respect for African peoples. Westerners said that they believed in democracy, equality, and political freedom, but they did not apply these values in the colonies. There were few democratic institutions. For many Africans, colonialism had meant the loss of their farmlands or terrible jobs on plantations or in sweatshops and factories. Middle-class Africans did not suffer as much as poor peasants and plantation workers, but they also had complaints. They usually qualified only for menial jobs in the government or business. Their salaries were lower than those of Europeans in similar jobs. Europeans set up segregated clubs, schools, and churches. Europeans also had a habit of addressing natives by their first names or calling an adult male "boy." For all of these reasons, educated Africans resented colonial rule and were determined to assert their own nationality. During the first part of the twentieth century, resentment turned to action. Educated African peoples began to organize political parties and movements seeking the end of foreign rule.

12. How did the new class of educated Africans feel about Western civilization and colonial rule?

_____

_____

_____

_____

_____

Reading Essentials and Study Guide

Chapter 6, Section 3

For use with textbook pages 354–359

BRITISH RULE IN INDIA

CONTENT VOCABULARY

sepoy an Indian soldier serving in the British army *(page 355)*

viceroy a governor who ruled as a representative of a monarch *(page 356)*

DRAWING FROM EXPERIENCE

Have you ever read any stories or poems by the British writer Rudyard Kipling? What insights do his stories and poems give us into life in India during the Age of Imperialism?

In the last two sections, you learned about imperialism in Southeast Asia and Africa. In this section, you will learn about the British Empire in India.

ORGANIZING YOUR THOUGHTS

Use the diagram below to help you take notes. British rule in India had both benefits and costs for the Indian people. List four benefits and four costs of the British rule.

California History Social Science Standards

10.4 Students analyze patterns of global change in the era of New Imperialism in at least two of the following regions or countries: Africa, Southeast Asia, China, India, Latin America and the Philippines.

Focuses on:
10.4.2, 10.4.3, 10.4.4

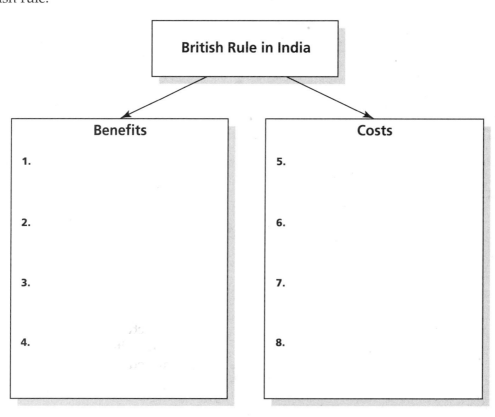

British Rule in India

Benefits

1.

2.

3.

4.

Costs

5.

6.

7.

8.

Reading Essentials and Study Guide

Chapter 6, Section 3 *(continued)*

READ TO LEARN

• The Sepoy Mutiny *(page 355)*

Over the course of the eighteenth century, British power in India had increased while the power of the Mogul rulers had declined. The British East India Company was given power by the British government to rule India. The British had the <u>attitude</u> that their culture was superior to Indian culture. The British East India Company had its own soldiers and forts. It also hired Indian soldiers, known as **sepoys,** to protect its interests.

> **Academic Vocabulary**
>
> **attitude:** a belief about something or someone (p. 355)

In 1857, the Indians' distrust of the British led to a revolt. The revolt was known to the British as the Great Rebellion or the Sepoy Mutiny. Indians call it the First War of Independence. The immediate cause of the revolt was a rumor that the British were issuing their Indian troops new bullets that were greased with cow and pig fat. The cow was sacred to Hindus. The pig was taboo to Muslims. A group of sepoys refused to load their rifles with the new bullets. When the British arrested them, the sepoys went on a rampage. They killed 50 Europeans. The revolt quickly spread. The Indian troops fought bravely but were not well organized. Rivalries between Hindus and Muslims kept Indians from working together. Within a year, the revolt was crushed. As a result of the revolt, the British Parliament <u>transferred</u> the powers of the East India Company directly to the British government. In 1876, Queen Victoria was given the title of Empress of India.

> **Academic Vocabulary**
>
> **transfer:** to move control from one person or group to another (p. 355)

9. What was the immediate cause of the Sepoy Mutiny?

_____

_____

_____

_____

• Colonial Rule *(page 356)*

The British government ruled India directly through a British official known as a **viceroy** (a governor who ruled as a representative of a monarch). British rule had both benefits and costs for the Indian people. There were four main benefits. British rule brought order and stability to India. It also led to a fairly honest and efficient government. A new school system was set up. Its goal was to train Indian children to serve in the government and army, but only elite, upper-class Indians could attend. Finally, the British brought railroads, the telegraph, and a postal service to India.

British rule also had costs for the Indian people. British manufactured goods destroyed local industries. For example, the introduction of British textiles put thousands of women out of work and severely damaged the

Reading Essentials and Study Guide

Chapter 6, Section 3 *(continued)*

Indian textile industry. In rural areas, the British sent the zamindars to collect taxes. The zamindars took advantage of their new authority and increased taxes. This forced many peasants to become tenants or lose their land entirely. The British also encouraged many farmers to switch from growing food to growing cotton. As a result, food supplies could not keep up with the growing population. Between 1800 and 1900, 30 million Indians died of starvation. Finally, British rule was degrading. The best jobs and the best housing were reserved for the British. Despite their education, the Indians were never considered equals of the British. The British were also disrespectful of India's cultural heritage.

10. Why did 30 million Indians die of starvation between 1800 and 1900?

_____

_____

_____

_____

- **An Indian Nationalist Movement** *(page 358)*

British racial attitudes led to the rise of an Indian nationalist movement. The first Indian nationalists were upper class and English-educated. Some were trained in British law and were members of the civil service. In 1885, a small group of Indians formed the Indian National Congress (INC). The INC did not demand immediate independence, but did call for a share in the governing process. The INC had difficulties because of religious differences. Many of its leaders were Hindu and reflected Hindu concerns. Muslims began to call for the creation of a separate Muslim League to represent the interests of the Muslims in India.

In 1915, Mohandas Gandhi brought new life to India's struggle for independence. Gandhi was born in India but studied in London. He became a lawyer and went to South Africa. After he returned to India, he became active in the independence movement. He set up a movement based on nonviolent resistance. It had two goals: to force the British to improve the lot of the poor and to gain independence for India.

11. What were the goals of Gandhi's movement?

_____

_____

_____

_____

Reading Essentials and Study Guide

Chapter 6, Section 3 (continued)

• Colonial Indian Culture (page 358)

A cultural revival took place in India in the early nineteenth century. It began with the creation of a British college in Calcutta. A local publishing house was soon opened. It printed textbooks on various subjects, as well as grammars and dictionaries in the Indian languages. The revival soon spread to other regions of India. Indian novelists and poets began writing historical romances and epics. Most preferred to use their own regional languages rather than English. The most famous Indian author was Rabindranath Tagore. He was also a social reformer, spiritual leader, educator, and philosopher. Tagore's life mission was to promote national pride. Tagore was more than just an Indian nationalist, however. He worked for human dignity, world peace, and the mutual understanding between East and West.

12. How did the cultural revival in India in the nineteenth century begin?

_____

_____

_____

_____

_____

Reading Essentials and Study Guide

Chapter 6, Section 4

For use with textbook pages 362–369

NATION BUILDING IN LATIN AMERICA

CONTENT VOCABULARY

creole a person of European descent who was born in Latin America and who lived there permanently *(page 363)*

peninsulare a Spanish or Portuguese official who resided temporarily in Latin America for political and economic gain *(page 363)*

mestizo a person of European and Indian descent *(page 364)*

Monroe Doctrine a doctrine issued by U.S. President James Monroe in which he guaranteed the independence of the new Latin American nations and warned against any European intervention in the Americas *(page 365)*

caudillo a Latin American leader who ruled chiefly by military force *(page 365)*

DRAWING FROM EXPERIENCE

Have you ever been to Texas? Did you know that Texas was once an independent country? How did Texas become a U.S. state?

In the last three sections, you read about European imperialism. In this section, you will learn how most of the countries of Latin America gained their independence from Spain and Portugal in the nineteenth century.

ORGANIZING YOUR THOUGHTS

Use the time line below to help you take notes. Indicate which Latin American countries gained their independence in the following years.

> **California History Social Science Standards**
>
> **10.2** Students compare and contrast the Glorious Revolution of England, the American Revolution, and the French Revolution and their enduring effects worldwide on the political expectations for self-government and individual liberty.
>
> **10.4** Students analyze patterns of global change in the era of New Imperialism in at least two of the following regions or countries: Africa, Southeast Asia, China, India, Latin America and the Philippines.
>
> **Focuses on:**
> 10.2.1, 10.2.3, 10.4.1, 10.4.2

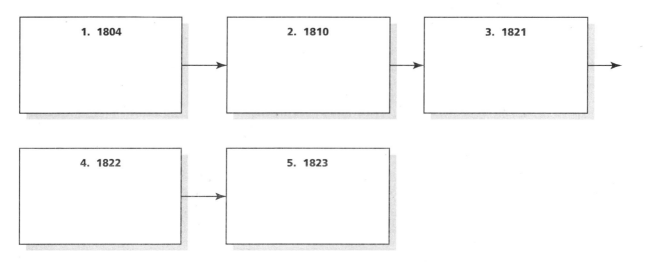

1. 1804   2. 1810   3. 1821

4. 1822   5. 1823

Name _____ Date _____ Class _____

Reading Essentials and Study Guide

Chapter 6, Section 4 (continued)

Copyright © by The McGraw-Hill Companies, Inc.

READ TO LEARN

• Nationalist Revolts (page 363)

Social classes divided colonial Latin America. At the top were *peninsulares*, who held all of the important positions. *Peninsulares* were Spanish and Portuguese officials who resided temporarily in Latin America for political and economic gain and then returned to their mother countries. **Creoles** were descendants of Europeans born in Latin America and lived there permanently. They controlled land and business but were regarded as second class citizens by *peninsulares*. **Mestizos** (people of European and Indian descent) were the largest group but worked as servants or laborers.

Creoles found the principles of equality of all people, free trade, and free press very attractive. They deeply resented the *peninsulares*. The creole elites began to denounce the rule of the Spanish and Portuguese. When Napoleon overthrew the monarchies of Spain and Portugal, the authority of the Spanish and Portuguese in their colonies was weakened. Between 1807 and 1825, revolutionary movements were able to succeed against the Spanish and Portuguese. Most of Latin America became independent.

Before these revolts, an unusual revolution took place in the French colony of Saint Domingue on the island of Hispaniola. Led by François-Dominique Toussaint-Louverture, more than a hundred thousand slaves revolted and took control of Hispaniola. On January 1, 1804, the western part of Hispaniola (now called Haiti) announced its freedom and became the first independent state in Latin America.

Beginning in 1810, Mexico also experienced a revolt. The first real hero of Mexican independence was Miguel Hidalgo, a parish priest. Hidalgo had studied the French Revolution and encouraged the local Indians and mestizos to free themselves from the Spanish. On September 16, 1810, a crowd of Indians and mestizos formed a mob army to attack the Spaniards. The revolt was crushed, and Hidalgo was sentenced to death, but September 16 is still remembered as Mexico's Independence Day. The creoles and *peninsulares* were both frightened by the Indians and mestizos. They cooperated in defeating the revolutionaries. Then the creoles and *peninsulares* decided to overthrow Spanish rule to preserve their own power. They selected a creole military leader, Agustín de Iturbide, as their leader. In 1821, Mexico declared its independence from Spain. Iturbide named himself emperor in 1822 but was deposed in 1823. Mexico then became a republic.

José de San Martín of Argentina and Simón Bolívar of Venezuela have been called the "Liberators of South America." They led revolutions throughout the continent. San Martín believed that the Spaniards must be removed from all of South America if any South American nation was to be free. By 1810, his forces had liberated Argentina. Bolívar began the struggle for independence in Venezuela and then went on to lead revolts in New Granada (Colombia) and Ecuador.

Reading Essentials and Study Guide

Chapter 6, Section 4 (continued)

In January 1817, San Martín led his forces over the Andes to attack the Spanish in Chile. The Spanish were badly defeated at the Battle of Chacabuco on February 12, 1817. Then San Martín moved on to Peru, where he was joined by Bolívar and his forces. The last significant Spanish army was crushed at Ayacucho on December 9, 1824. By the end of 1824, Peru, Uruguay, Paraguay, Colombia, Venezuela, Argentina, Bolivia, and Chile had all become free of Spain. Earlier, in 1822, Brazil had gained its independence from Portugal. The Central American states had become independent in 1823. In 1838 and 1839, they divided into five republics: Guatemala, El Salvador, Honduras, Costa Rica, and Nicaragua.

There was still one threat to the independence of the Latin American states. Members of the Concert of Europe wanted to use troops to restore Spanish control of Latin America. The British disagreed, because they wanted to trade with Latin America. They joined with the United States against any European moves in Latin America. In 1823, United States President James Monroe issued the **Monroe Doctrine.** He guaranteed the independence of the new Latin American nations and warned against any European intervention in the Americas.

6. Who were the "Liberators of South America"?

_____

_____

_____

• Difficulties of Nation Building (page 365)

The new Latin American nations had serious problems after they gained their independence. Many people had been killed, and much livestock and property had been destroyed. The new nations were not sure of their exact boundaries and went to war with each other to settle border disputes. Poor roads, a lack of railroads, thick jungles, and mountains were also problems. They made communication, transportation, and national unity difficult.

Soon after independence, strong leaders known as **caudillos** came into power in many countries. Caudillos ruled chiefly by military force and were usually supported by large landowners. Some caudillos were modernizers who built roads, canals, ports, and schools. Others were destructive. Antonio López de Santa Anna, for example, ruled Mexico from 1833 to 1855. He misused state funds, stopped reforms, and created chaos. In 1835, American settlers in the Mexican state of Texas revolted against Santa Anna's rule. Texas gained its independence in 1836 and United States statehood in 1845. War between Mexico and the United States soon followed (1846–1848). Mexico was defeated and lost almost one-half of its territory to the United States in the Mexican War. Santa Anna's rule was followed by a period of reform from 1855 to 1876. This era was dominated by Benito Juárez. He brought liberal reforms

Academic Vocabulary
dominate: to rule or control (p. 363)

Reading Essentials and Study Guide

Chapter 6, Section 4 (continued)

to Mexico, including separation of church and state, land distribution to the poor, and an educational system for all of Mexico.

Some caudillos, such as Juan Manual de Rosas in Argentina, were supported by the masses and brought about radical change. Unfortunately, the caudillo's authority depended on his personal power. When he died or lost power, civil wars for control of the country often erupted.

Great Britain now dominated the Latin American economy. British merchants moved into Latin America in large numbers. Latin America continued to serve as a source of raw materials and food for the industrial nations of Europe and the United States. Exports included wheat, tobacco, wool, sugar, coffee, and hides. Manufactured goods were imported, especially textiles. The <u>emphasis</u> on exporting raw materials and importing manufactured goods meant that the Latin American economy continued to be dominated by foreigners.

Academic Vocabulary
emphasis: to place importance on something (p. 367)

A fundamental problem for all of the new Latin American nations was the domination of society by large landowners. Their estates were often so large that they could not be farmed efficiently. Land was the basis of wealth, social prestige, and political power. The large landowners ran governments and controlled courts. They made huge profits by growing export crops, such as coffee. The masses had no land to grow basic food crops and experienced terrible poverty.

7. In what ways were large landowners a fundamental problem for the new Latin American nations?

_____

_____

_____

• Political Change in Latin America (page 368)

After 1870, Latin American governments wrote constitutions similar to those of the United States and European democracies. However, the large landowners limited voting rights in order to keep their power.

By 1900, the United States had begun to interfere in the affairs of many Latin American nations. As a result of the Spanish-American War (1898), Cuba became a United States protectorate, and Puerto Rico was annexed to the United States. In 1903, the United States supported a rebellion that made it possible for Panama to separate itself from Colombia. In return, the United States was granted control of a strip of land 10 miles wide that ran from coast to coast in Panama. The United States built the Panama Canal there.

Americans began to invest in Latin America. Beginning in 1898, American military forces were sent to Cuba, Mexico, Guatemala, Honduras, Nicaragua,

Reading Essentials and Study Guide

Chapter 6, Section 4 *(continued)*

Panama, Colombia, Haiti, and the Dominican Republic to protect American interests. Some of these troops remained for many years. Many Latin Americans began to resent U.S. interference.

In some countries, large landowners supported dictators who looked out for their interests. Porfirio Díaz, for example, ruled Mexico between 1877 and 1911. He came to power with the support of the army, foreign capitalists, large landowners, and the Catholic Church. During his reign, the wages of workers declined. 95 percent of the rural population owned no land. About a thousand families owned almost all of Mexico. After Díaz was forced from power, Emiliano Zapata aroused the landless peasants and began to seize the estates of wealthy landowners. Between 1910 and 1920, the Mexican Revolution caused great damage to the Mexican economy. Finally, a new constitution was enacted in 1917. It set up a government led by a president. It also created land-reform policies, set limits on foreign investments, and had an agenda to help the workers.

8. Why did the United States support the rebellion in Panama?

_____

_____

_____

- **Economic Change in Latin America** *(page 369)*

After 1870, a period of prosperity began in Latin America. It was based to a large extent on the export of a few basic items. These included wheat and beef from Argentina, coffee from Brazil, coffee and bananas from Central America, and sugar and silver from Peru. After 1900, Latin Americans also increased their own industrialization, especially by building textile, food-processing, and construction material factories.

One result of this prosperity was growth in the middle sectors (divisions) of Latin American society. These sectors, which included lawyers, merchants, shopkeepers, businesspeople, schoolteachers, professors, bureaucrats, and military officers, continued to <u>expand</u> after 1900. These middle-class Latin Americans lived in the cities, believed in education, and saw the United States as a model, especially in regard to industrialization. They sought liberal reform, not revolution. Once they had the right to vote, they usually sided with the landholding elites.

Academic Vocabulary
expand: to increase the number or volume of something (p. 369)

9. What were some characteristics of middle-class Latin Americans?

_____

_____

_____

Reading Essentials and Study Guide

Chapter 7, Section 1

For use with textbook pages 379–386

THE DECLINE OF THE QING DYNASTY

CONTENT VOCABULARY

extraterritoriality living in a foreign country without being subject to its laws *(page 381)*

self-strengthening a policy in China in the late nineteenth and early twentieth centuries that encouraged the adoption of Western technology, while keeping Confucian values and institutions *(page 383)*

spheres of influence areas in China where imperial powers had exclusive trading rights *(page 384)*

Open Door Policy a proposal that ensured equal access to the Chinese market for all nations and preserved the unity of the Chinese Empire *(p. 385)*

indemnity a payment for damages *(page 386)*

DRAWING FROM EXPERIENCE

Do you like change? Why do you think many people are resistant to change?

In this section, you will read about the decline of the Qing dynasty in China. As the Qing dynasty declined, some Chinese leaders pushed for reforms, but others were resistant to change.

ORGANIZING YOUR THOUGHTS

Use the diagram below to help you take notes. The decline of the Qing dynasty was the result of internal problems within China, as well as external pressures by Western countries. List four of the internal problems that caused the Qing dynasty to decline.

California History Social Science Standards
10.4 Students analyze patterns of global change in the era of New Imperialism in at least two of the following regions or countries: Africa, Southeast Asia, China, India, Latin America and the Philippines.
Focuses on: 10.4.2, 10.4.3

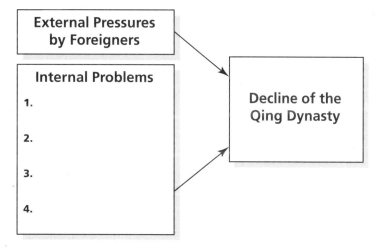

Reading Essentials and Study Guide

Chapter 7, Section 1 *(continued)*

READ TO LEARN

• Causes of Decline *(page 380)*

In 1800, the Qing dynasty was at the height of its power. During the next hundred years, however, it declined and collapsed. One important reason for the <u>decline</u> was external pressure from Westerners. But internal problems also played a role in its decline. The Qing dynasty began to have problems with corruption, peasant unrest, and incompetence. Population growth made things worse. By 1900, there were 400 million people in China. Population growth created a serious food shortage, and many people died of hunger.

> **Academic Vocabulary**
>
> **decline:** to move toward an inferior state or weaker condition (p. 380)

5. How did population growth contribute to the decline of the Qing dynasty?

_____

_____

_____

_____

_____

• The Opium War *(page 380)*

By 1800, Europeans had been in contact with China for more than two hundred years. But European merchants were restricted to a small trading post at Guangzhou (Canton). The British did not like this arrangement. The British also had a trade imbalance in China. Britain imported tea, silk, and porcelain from the Chinese and sent Indian cotton to China to pay for these imports. But the cotton did not cover all of the imports, and the British had to pay for more and more of the imports with silver. To improve their trade balance, the British began to trade opium with the Chinese. Opium is a highly addictive drug that was grown in northern India. The Chinese government had already seen how dangerous opium was and had made the opium trade illegal. They asked the British government to stop the opium trade, but the British refused. The Chinese government then blockaded the foreign area in Guangzhou so that they could seize the opium before it came into the country. The British responded with force, which started the first Opium War (1839–1842).

The Chinese were no match for the British. British warships destroyed Chinese forts and sailed up the Chang Jiang (Yangtze River). The Qing dynasty decided to make peace with the British. In the Treaty of Nanjing in 1842, the Chinese agreed to open five coastal ports to British trade. In these ports, Europeans lived in their own sections and were subject to their own laws, not to Chinese laws. This practice is known as **extraterritoriality.** The Chinese also agreed to limit taxes on imported British goods and to pay for the costs of the war. China also gave the island of Hong Kong to the British. Nothing was said in the treaty about the opium trade.

Reading Essentials and Study Guide

Chapter 7, Section 1 (continued)

6. Why did the British begin to trade opium with China?

_____

_____

_____

_____

_____

- ## The Tai Ping Rebellion *(page 382)*

The Chinese government was unable to deal with the economic problems at the time. This led to a peasant revolt, known as the Tai Ping Rebellion (1850–1864). Hong Xiuquan, a Christian convert, led it. He believed that God had given him the mission of destroying the Qing dynasty. He was joined by many peasants and captured the town of Yongan. He then proclaimed a new dynasty, the Heavenly Kingdom of Great Peace (Tai Ping Tianguo). The Tai Ping Rebellion had several goals. These goals included giving land to all peasants and treating women as equals of men. People were also required to give up their private possessions. Money, food, and clothing were to be shared equally by all. Hong outlawed alcohol and tobacco and the practice of binding women's feet. In March 1853, the rebels seized Nanjing and killed 25,000 people. The revolt continued for 10 more years but gradually began to fall apart. Europeans came to the aid of the Qing dynasty. In 1864, Chinese forces recaptured Nanjing and destroyed the rebel forces. By the end of the rebellion, 20 million people had been killed.

Their struggle with Western powers made it hard for the Qing dynasty to deal with internal unrest. Beginning in 1856, Great Britain and France used force to expand their trading privileges. In the Treaty of Tianjin of 1858, the Chinese agreed to legalize the opium trade and open new ports to foreign trade. They also gave up the Kowloon peninsula to Britain. When the Chinese resisted parts of the treaty, the British seized Beijing.

7. What were some of the goals of the Tai Ping Rebellion?

_____

_____

_____

_____

_____

Reading Essentials and Study Guide

Chapter 7, Section 1 *(continued)*

- ### Efforts at Reform *(page 383)*

During the Tai Ping Rebellion, China's government had relied on regional warlords to recruit the troops necessary to restore order. To pay their armies, warlords had collected taxes from local people. After the rebellion was over, many warlords continued to collect taxes for their own use.

The Qing dynasty finally began to listen to reformers. The reformers wanted a new policy that they called **"self-strengthening."** This meant that China should adopt Western technology while keeping Confucian values and institutions. This became the basis for China's foreign and domestic policy for the next 25 years. Railroads, weapons factories, and shipyards were built, but the Chinese value system remained unchanged.

8. What reforms did the Qing dynasty begin to make in the late 1870s?

_____

_____

_____

_____

_____

- ### The Advance of Imperialism *(page 384)*

Russia took advantage of China's weakness to force it to give up territories north of the Amur River in Siberia. In Tibet, Russia and Great Britain struggled for control. This allowed Tibet to become free from Chinese influence.

European countries began to create **spheres of influence** in China. These were areas where the imperial powers had exclusive trading rights. After the Tai Ping Rebellion, warlords began to negotiate directly with foreign nations. In return for money, the warlords gave these nations exclusive trading rights or railroad-building or mining privileges. Britain, France, Germany, Russia, and Japan all established spheres of influence in China.

In 1894, China went to war with Japan over Japanese involvement in Korea. The Chinese were defeated. Japan demanded and received the island of Taiwan and the Liaodong Peninsula. But European powers forced Japan to give the Liaodong Peninsula back to China. In 1897, two German missionaries in China were murdered. Germany used this pretext to demand territories in the Shandong Peninsula. China gave these territories to Germany. As a result, other European nations began to make new claims on Chinese territory.

In June 1898, the young emperor Guang Xu started a reform program based on changes in Japan. During the following weeks, known as the One Hundred Days of Reform, he issued edicts calling for major political, administrative, and educational reforms. Many conservatives opposed these reforms.

Reading Essentials and Study Guide

Chapter 7, Section 1 *(continued)*

The emperor's aunt, Empress Dowager Ci Xi, also opposed the reforms. With the aid of the imperial army, she was able to imprison the emperor and end his reform efforts.

9. Why did the reform efforts of Guang Xu fail?

_____

_____

_____

_____

_____

• Opening the Door to China *(page 385)*

Great Britain and the United States became afraid that other nations would overrun China if the Chinese government collapsed. In 1899, U.S. secretary of state John Hay presented a proposal that <u>ensured</u> equal access to the Chinese market for all nations. It also preserved the unity of the Chinese Empire. When none of the other governments opposed the idea, Hay proclaimed that all major nations had agreed that China should have an Open Door policy.

Academic Vocabulary
ensure: to make certain or safe (p. 385)

The Open Door policy did not end the system of spheres of influence. But it loosened restrictions on trade among the imperialist powers within the spheres. The policy also lessened fears in Britain, France, Germany, and Russia that other powers would take advantage of China's weakness and try to dominate the Chinese market.

10. What was the Open Door policy? What were some of its effects?

_____

_____

_____

_____

Reading Essentials and Study Guide

Chapter 7, Section 1 (continued)

- ### The Boxer Rebellion (page 386)

The Open Door policy did not stop the Boxer Rebellion. *Boxer* was the popular name for members of a secret organization called the Society of the Harmonious Fists. The Boxers were upset by the foreign takeover of Chinese lands. Their slogan was "destroy the foreigner." They especially disliked Christian missionaries and Chinese converts to Christianity. At the beginning of 1900, Boxers roamed the countryside and killed missionaries and Chinese Christians. Their victims also included foreign businessmen and even the German envoy to Beijing. In response to the killings, an allied army of 20,000 British, French, German, Russian, American, and Japanese troops attacked Beijing in August 1900. The army restored order and demanded more concessions from the Chinese government. The Chinese government was forced to pay a heavy **indemnity** (a payment for damages) to the nations that had crushed the rebellion.

11. Who were the Boxers? Why were they upset?

_____

_____

_____

_____

_____

Reading Essentials and Study Guide

Chapter 7, Section 2

For use with textbook pages 387–393

REVOLUTION IN CHINA

CONTENT VOCABULARY

provincial local, as opposed to national *(page 388)*

commodity a marketable product *(page 391)*

DRAWING FROM EXPERIENCE

Have you ever read any books about China? What are some customs or traditions in China? How are they the same or different from your family's customs or traditions?

In the last section, you read about the decline of the Qing dynasty. In this section, you will learn about the fall of the Qing dynasty in the early twentieth century, and the changes in Chinese society and culture during this time.

> **California History Social Science Standards**
>
> **10.4** Students analyze patterns of global change in the era of New Imperialism in at least two of the following regions or countries: Africa, Southeast Asia, China, India, Latin America and the Philippines.
>
> **Focuses on:**
> 10.4.1, 10.4.4

ORGANIZING YOUR THOUGHTS

Use the diagram below to help you take notes. The coming of Westerners dramatically affected China. List three ways that the Chinese economy was affected by Westerners. Also list three ways that the West influenced Chinese culture.

Effect of Westerners

Chinese Economy

1.

2.

3.

Chinese Culture

4.

5.

6.

Reading Essentials and Study Guide

Chapter 7, Section 2 *(continued)*

READ TO LEARN

• The Fall of the Qing *(page 388)*

After the Boxer Rebellion, the Qing dynasty tried to make reforms. The civil service examination system was replaced by a new educational system based on the Western model. In 1909, legislative assemblies were formed at the **provincial** (local) level. Elections for a national assembly were held in 1910. Reformers soon became angry, however, when they discovered that the new assemblies could not pass laws but could only give advice to the ruler. The reforms also did nothing for the peasants, artisans, and miners. Their living conditions were getting worse because of tax increases. Unrest grew in the countryside.

The first signs of revolution appeared during the last decade of the nineteenth century. A young radical, Sun Yat-sen, formed the Revive China Society. Sun believed that the Qing dynasty could no longer govern the country. But he knew that the Chinese people were not ready for democracy. He developed a reform process that had three stages: a military takeover, a transitional phase in which Sun's own revolutionary party would prepare the people for democratic rule, and the final stage of a constitutional democracy. In 1905, Sun united radical groups across China and formed the Revolutionary Alliance.

In 1908, Empress Dowager Ci Xi died. The throne now passed to China's "last emperor," Henry Pu Yi, who was an infant. In October 1911, followers of Sun Yat-sen launched an uprising in central China. The Qing dynasty collapsed, but Sun's party did not have the military or political power to form a new government. The party was forced to turn to General Yuan Shigai, who controlled the army. He agreed to serve as president of a new Chinese republic.

7. What were the three stages of reform proposed by Sun Yat-sen?

_____

_____

_____

_____

_____

• An Era of Civil War *(page 390)*

After the collapse of the Qing dynasty, the military took over. General Yuan Shigai ruled in a traditional way and even tried to set up a new imperial dynasty. Reformers hated him because he used murder and terror to destroy the new democratic institutions. He was hated by traditionalists for being disloyal to the Qing dynasty. He came into conflict with Sun's party, now called

Reading Essentials and Study Guide

Chapter 7, Section 2 *(continued)*

the Guomindang, or Nationalist Party. When Yuan dissolved the new parliament, the Nationalists started a rebellion. The rebellion failed, and Sun Yat-sen fled to Japan.

General Yuan died in 1916 and was succeeded by one of his officers. For the next several years, China slipped into civil war. Warlords seized power in the provinces. Their soldiers caused massive destruction throughout China.

8. Why was General Yuan Shigai so unpopular?

_____

_____

_____

_____

_____

• Chinese Society in Transition *(page 391)*

In the mid-1800's China was in a state of <u>transition</u>. The coming of Westerners to China affected the Chinese economy in three ways. Westerners introduced modern means of transportation and communication. They also created an export market and <u>integrated</u> the Chinese economy into the world economy. The growth of industry and trade was especially noticeable in the cities. A national market for **commodities** (marketable products), such as oil, copper, salt, tea, and porcelain, had developed. New crops brought in from other countries increased food production. To some, these changes were beneficial. Western influences forced the Chinese to adopt new ways of thinking and acting. But China paid a heavy price for the new ways. Its local industry was largely destroyed. Many of the profits in the new economy went to foreign countries.

After World War I, Chinese businesspeople began to develop new ventures. Shanghai, Wuhan, Tianjin, and Guangzhou became major industrial and commercial centers with a growing middle class and an industrial working class.

Academic Vocabulary
transition: a subtle change from one state or place to another (p. 391)

Academic Vocabulary
integrate: to incorporate into a larger unit (p. 391)

9. In what ways did the coming of Westerners have a negative effect on the Chinese economy?

_____

_____

_____

_____

Reading Essentials and Study Guide

Chapter 7, Section 2 *(continued)*

• China's Changing Culture *(page 392)*

In 1800, daily life for most Chinese people was the same as it had been for centuries. Most were farmers, living in villages in rice fields and on hillsides. 125 years later, there was a different society in China. The changes were most obvious in the cities. The educated and wealthy in the cities had been affected by the presence of Westerners in the country. Confucian social ideals were declining. Radical reformers wanted to eliminate traditional culture. They wanted to create a new China that would be respected by the modern world.

The first changes in traditional culture came in the late nineteenth century. Intellectuals began to introduce Western books, paintings, music, and ideas to China. Western literature and art became popular in China, especially among the urban middle class. Most creative artists followed foreign trends, although traditionalists held on to Chinese culture. Literature in particular was influenced by foreign ideas. Most Chinese novels written after World War I dealt with Chinese subjects, but they reflected the Western tendency toward realism. Most of China's modern authors also showed a clear contempt for the past. Ba Jin was one of China's foremost writers at the turn of the century. In his trilogy, *Family, Spring,* and *Autumn,* he describes the disintegration of traditional Confucian ways as the younger members of a large family attempt to break away from their elders.

10. In what ways was Chinese literature particularly influenced by foreign ideas?

_____

_____

_____

_____

Reading Essentials and Study Guide

Chapter 7, Section 3

For use with textbook pages 396–403

RISE OF MODERN JAPAN

CONTENT VOCABULARY
concession a political compromise *(page 397)*
prefecture a territory in Japan during the Meiji government *(page 398)*

DRAWING FROM EXPERIENCE

What is the first thing that comes to mind when you hear the word "Japanese"? Do you think first of Japanese products, such as cars? Or do you think first of events in Japanese history, such as World War II?

In the last two sections, you learned about changes in China during the late nineteenth and early twentieth centuries. In this section, you will learn about changes in Japan during the same period.

California History Social Science Standards

10.4 Students analyze patterns of global change in the era of New Imperialism in at least two of the following regions or countries: Africa, Southeast Asia, China, India, Latin America and the Philippines.

Focuses on:
10.4.1, 10.4.3, 10.4.4

ORGANIZING YOUR THOUGHTS

Use the diagram below to help you take notes. Under the Meiji Constitution of 1889, the Japanese government was divided into an executive branch and a legislative branch. Describe the structure of these two branches of government and how officials in each branch were appointed or elected. Circle the branch of government that had the most authority.

Political Structure Under the Meiji Constitution

Executive Branch

1.

Legislative Branch

2.

Reading Essentials and Study Guide

Chapter 7, Section 3 *(continued)*

READ TO LEARN

• An End to Isolation *(page 397)*

By 1800, the Tokugawa shogunate had ruled the Japanese islands for two hundred years. It had driven out foreign traders and missionaries and isolated the country from nearly all contact with the outside world. To the Western powers, Japanese isolation was a challenge. They began to approach Japan in the hope of opening it up to foreign economic interests. The first foreign power to succeed with Japan was the United States. In the summer of 1853, an American fleet of warships under Commodore Matthew Perry arrived in Edo Bay (now Tokyo Bay). Perry brought with him a letter from President Millard Fillmore. The U.S. president asked for better treatment of sailors shipwrecked on the Japanese islands. He also requested the opening of relations between the United States and Japan.

About six months later, Perry returned to Japan for an answer. Shogunate officials had been discussing the issue. Some argued that contacts with the West would hurt Japan. Others feared the military superiority of the United States and recommended **concessions** (political compromises). Under pressure from Perry's warships, Japan agreed to the Treaty of Kanagawa. This treaty provided for the return of shipwrecked sailors, the opening of two ports to Western traders, and the establishment of a U.S. consulate in Japan. In 1858, U.S. consul Townsend Harris signed a more detailed treaty. It opened several new ports to the United States. It also provided for an exchange of ministers. Similar treaties were soon signed by Japan and several other European nations.

3. What attitude did the Tokugawa shogunate have toward the outside world prior to the nineteenth century?

_____

_____

_____

_____

_____

_____

• Resistance to the New Order *(page 398)*

The decision to open relations with Western nations was very unpopular in parts of Japan. Resistance was especially strong among the samurai warriors in two territories in the south, Satsuma and Choshu. Both territories had strong military traditions and had not been exposed to Western military pressure.

Reading Essentials and Study Guide

Chapter 7, Section 3 (continued)

In 1863, the Sat-Cho (Satsuma-Choshu) alliance made the shogun promise to end relations with the West. In January 1868, the Sat-Cho armies attacked the shogun's palace and proclaimed that the authority of the emperor had been restored. After a few weeks, the shogun's forces collapsed. The shogunate system came to an end.

4. In what parts of Japan was the decision to open relations with the West particularly unpopular? Why?

_____

_____

_____

_____

_____

_____

• The Meiji Restoration (page 398)

The Sat-Cho leaders realized that Japan must change to survive. They began a policy of reform that turned Japan into a modern industrial nation. The symbol of the new era was the young emperor Mutsuhito. He called his reign the Meiji ("Enlightened Rule"). This period became known as the Meiji Restoration. The Sat-Cho leaders controlled the Meiji ruler, just as earlier emperors had been controlled by the shogunate. The capital was moved from Kyoto to Edo (now Tokyo). To reduce the power of the daimyo, the new leaders stripped them of the titles to their lands in 1871. As compensation, the daimyo were given government bonds and were named governors of the territories that had been under their control. The territories were now called **prefectures.**

During the next 20 years, the Meiji government studied Western political systems. The Meiji Constitution of 1889 was modeled after the constitution of Imperial Germany. The executive branch had the most authority. In theory, the emperor had all executive authority. In practice, a prime minister and his cabinet of ministers had the real executive authority. The Meiji leaders picked these ministers. The legislative branch consisted of a parliament with two houses. Members of the upper house included royal appointments and elected nobles, while members of the lower house were elected. The two houses were to have equal powers. The final result was a political system that was democratic in form, but authoritarian in practice. Power remained in the hands of the Sat-Cho leaders. The system allowed the traditional ruling class to keep its influence and economic power.

Reading Essentials and Study Guide

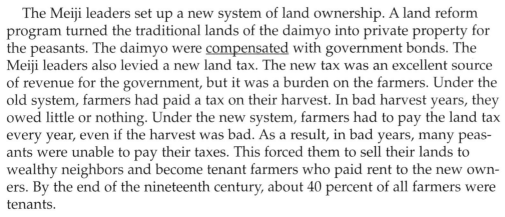

Chapter 7, Section 3 (continued)

The Meiji leaders set up a new system of land ownership. A land reform program turned the traditional lands of the daimyo into private property for the peasants. The daimyo were <u>compensated</u> with government bonds. The Meiji leaders also levied a new land tax. The new tax was an excellent source of revenue for the government, but it was a burden on the farmers. Under the old system, farmers had paid a tax on their harvest. In bad harvest years, they owed little or nothing. Under the new system, farmers had to pay the land tax every year, even if the harvest was bad. As a result, in bad years, many peasants were unable to pay their taxes. This forced them to sell their lands to wealthy neighbors and become tenant farmers who paid rent to the new owners. By the end of the nineteenth century, about 40 percent of all farmers were tenants.

The Meiji government encouraged the development of new industries. It gave subsidies to industries and provided training and foreign advisers. It also improved transportation and communications and started a new educational system that stressed applied science. By 1900, Japan's industrial sector was beginning to grow. Besides tea and silk, other key industries were weapons, shipbuilding, and sake (Japanese rice wine).

The Meiji reformers also focused on the military. The reformers were well aware that Japan would need a modern army to compete with the Western powers. A new imperial army was formed in 1871. It was based on compulsory military service. All Japanese men served for three years. The new army was well <u>equipped</u> with modern weapons.

Education also changed. The education ministry adopted the American model of elementary schools, secondary schools, and universities. It brought foreign specialists to Japan, and sent bright students to study abroad. In the schools, a great deal of emphasis was still placed on the virtues of family and community. Loyalty to the emperor was especially valued.

The Meiji Restoration had a dramatic effect on the traditional social system in Japan. Special privileges for the aristocracy were abolished. Women were allowed to seek an education. As the economy shifted from an agricultural to an industrial base, many Japanese people began to get new jobs and establish new relationships. Western fashions, dancing, and sports became popular in Japan. Japanese young people began to imitate the clothing styles, eating habits, hairstyles, and social practices of European and American young people.

The Meiji Restoration had a less attractive side. Many commoners were exploited in the coal mines and textile mills. Workers labored up to 20 hours a day, often under terrible conditions. In many areas, villagers sought new political and human rights. A popular rights movement of the 1870s laid the groundwork for one of Japan's first political parties. It wanted a government that would do what the people wanted. The Civil Code of 1898, however, played down individual rights.

Academic Vocabulary

compensate: to make an appropriate and usually counterbalancing payment to (p. 399)

Academic Vocabulary

equip: to make ready for service or action by gathering the needed supplies (p. 400)

Reading Essentials and Study Guide

Chapter 7, Section 3 *(continued)*

5. What were some of the changes that the Meiji Restoration made in the areas of economics and education?

_____

_____

_____

_____

_____

_____

• Joining the Imperialist Nations *(page 401)*

The Japanese also copied Western imperialism. Japan is a small country that is densely populated and lacks resources. The Japanese felt that they needed to expand into other territories. They also believed that Western nations were wealthy and powerful because they had colonies. The Japanese began their expansion close to home. In 1874, Japan claimed control of the Ryukyu Islands. Two years later, Japan's navy forced the Koreans to open their ports to Japanese trade. During the 1880s, Chinese-Japanese rivalry over Korea grew. In 1894, Japan and China went to war. Japanese ships destroyed the Chinese fleet and seized the Manchurian city of Port Arthur. In the treaty that ended the war, China recognized the independence of Korea. They also ceded (transferred) Taiwan and the Liaodong Peninsula to Japan. The Japanese later returned the Liaodong Peninsula to China.

Russia was also interested in Korea. Rivalry over Korea led to strained relations between Japan and Russia. In 1904, Japan attacked the Russian naval base at Port Arthur, which Russia had taken from China in 1898. When Japanese forces moved into Manchuria and the Liaodong Peninsula, Russian troops were no match for them. The Japanese attacked in a continuous <u>succession</u> of waves. Russia sent its Baltic fleet to Japan, but the new Japanese navy defeated the Russian fleet. Russia agreed to a peace settlement in 1905. They gave the Liaodong Peninsula back to Japan. The Japanese victory stunned the world. Japan had become one of the great powers.

Academic Vocabulary
succession: a number of persons or things that follow each other in sequence (p. 402)

The Japanese government established a sphere of influence in Korea. In 1905, the United States recognized Japan's role in Korea and asked for Japan's support for American authority in the Philippines. However, suspicion between Japan and the United States was growing. In 1907, President Theodore Roosevelt made an agreement with Japan that essentially stopped Japanese immigration to the United States.

Reading Essentials and Study Guide

Chapter 7, Section 3 *(continued)*

6. Why did the Japanese think that expansion was necessary?

_____

_____

_____

_____

_____

_____

- **Culture in an Era of Transition** *(page 402)*

Western technology and ideas were introduced to Japan in the nineteenth century and greatly altered Japanese culture. Literature was especially affected. Japanese authors began translating and imitating European literature. Japanese novels were particularly influenced by Western realism. The Japanese also copied Western artistic techniques and styles. Huge buildings of steel and concrete, with Greek columns, appeared in many Japanese cities. A national reaction to these changes began by the end of the nineteenth century. Many Japanese artists began to return to older techniques. In 1889, the Tokyo School of Fine Arts was established to promote traditional Japanese art.

The cultural exchange went both ways. Japanese art influenced Western painters. Japanese arts and crafts, porcelains, textiles, fans, folding screens, and woodblock prints became fashionable in Europe and North America. Japanese gardens became especially popular in the United States.

7. How was Japanese culture affected by Western technology and ideas?

_____

_____

_____

_____

Reading Essentials and Study Guide

Chapter 8, Section 1

For use with textbook pages 421–425

THE ROAD TO WORLD WAR I

CONTENT VOCABULARY

conscription a military draft *(page 423)*

mobilization the process of assembling troops and supplies and making them ready for war *(page 425)*

DRAWING FROM EXPERIENCE

Have you ever been given an ultimatum? How did you react to the ultimatum?

In this section, you will learn about the events that led to the start of World War I. Ultimatums played an important role in starting World War I.

ORGANIZING YOUR THOUGHTS

Use the time line below to help you take notes. Identify seven key events during the summer of 1914 that led to World War I.

1.	2.	3.
June 28	**July 23**	**July 28**

4.	5.	6.
July 29	**Aug. 1**	**Aug. 3**

7.
Aug. 4

> **California History Social Science Standards**
>
> **10.5** Students analyze the causes and course of the First World War.
>
> **Focuses on:**
> 10.5.1, 10.5.2

Reading Essentials and Study Guide

Chapter 8, Section 1 *(continued)*

READ TO LEARN

- **Nationalism and the System of Alliances** *(page 422)*

The growth of nationalism in the nineteenth century had many serious results. Competition for colonies and trade increased. Europe's great powers were soon divided into two alliances, the Triple Alliance and the Triple Entente. Crises in the Balkans between 1908 and 1913 made many European nations angry with each other. They were willing to go to war to preserve the power of their national states. Not all <u>ethnic</u> groups had become nations. But the growth of nationalism made the Irish, the Poles, and the Slavic peoples dream of creating their own national states.

National desires were not the only reason for conflict in the early 1900s. The working and lower middle class wanted a bigger share of the economic wealth they had helped create. Trade unions demanded better wages. Socialist parties wanted an end to capitalism. Some conservative leaders were afraid that their nations were on the verge of revolution. Some historians believe that the fear of revolution and the desire to suppress internal conflicts encouraged the leaders of some nations to go to war in 1914.

After 1900, the size of armies throughout Europe grew at an alarming rate. **Conscription,** a military draft, was used by most Western nations before 1914. It caused the size of European armies to double between 1890 and 1914. Militarism (preparation for war) was growing. Military leaders became more powerful. They began to draw up plans that could be used if their countries went to war. They insisted that <u>altering</u> these plans would cause chaos in the military. In the 1914 crises, this forced European political leaders to make decisions for military rather than political reasons.

Academic Vocabulary
ethnic: of or relating to large groups of people belonging to the same racial, national, tribal, religious, linguistic, or cultural origin or background (p. 422)

Academic Vocabulary
alter: to give a different position, course, or direction to something or someone (p. 423)

8. What were some of the results of the growth of nationalism in the nineteenth century?

_____

_____

_____

_____

_____

Reading Essentials and Study Guide

Chapter 8, Section 1 (continued)

• The Outbreak of War: Summer 1914 (page 424)

Nationalism, internal conflicts, and militarism all played a role in the starting of World War I. But it was a crisis in the Balkans in the summer of 1914 that led directly to war. States in southeastern Europe had struggled for years to free themselves from Ottoman rule. Austria-Hungary and Russia both wanted to control these new nations. By 1914, Serbia, supported by Russia, was determined to create a large Slavic state in the Balkans. Austria-Hungary was determined that this would not happen. Many Europeans <u>anticipated</u> war.

On June 28, 1914, Archduke Francis Ferdinand, the heir to the throne of Austria-Hungary, visited the Bosnian city of Sarajevo. Members of the Black Hand made plans to kill him. The Black Hand was a Serbian terrorist organization that wanted Bosnia to be free of Austria-Hungary. An attempt to kill the archduke with a bomb was unsuccessful. Later in the day, however, Gavrilo Princep, a 19-year-old Bosnian Serb, shot and killed both the archduke and his wife.

The Austro-Hungarian government did not know whether the Serbian government was involved in the assassination of the archduke, but it did not care. It saw this as an opportunity to crush Serbia. Austrian leaders wanted to attack Serbia, but they feared that Russia would intervene on Serbia's <u>behalf</u>. The Austrians asked their German allies for help. Emperor William II of Germany agreed to give Austria-Hungary his full support. Austrian leaders sent an ultimatum to Serbia on July 23. Many of the demands were so extreme that Serbia had no choice but to reject some of them. On July 28, Austria-Hungary declared war on Serbia.

Russia was determined to support Serbia. Czar Nicholas II ordered partial mobilization of the Russian army. **Mobilization** is the process of assembling troops and supplies and making them ready for war. In 1914, mobilization was seen as an act of war. Russian military leaders told the czar that they could not partially mobilize. Their mobilization plans were based on a war against both Germany and Austria-Hungary. They claimed that mobilization against only Austria-Hungary would create chaos. Based on this claim, the czar ordered full mobilization of the Russian army on July 29. The German government warned Russia that it must stop its mobilization. When Russia refused, Germany declared war on Russia on August 1.

Academic Vocabulary
anticipate: to give advance thought to an action expected to occur (p. 424)

Academic Vocabulary
behalf: in the interest of something or someone else (p. 424)

Reading Essentials and Study Guide

Chapter 8, Section 1 *(continued)*

Germany also had a military plan. One of its generals, Alfred von Schlieffen, had drawn up a plan that called for war against both Russia and France. Under the Schlieffen Plan, Germany could not go to war against Russia only. As a result, Germany declared war on France on August 3. It also issued an ultimatum to Belgium, in which it demanded the right of German troops to pass through Belgium, even though Belgium was a neutral nation.

On August 4, Great Britain declared war on Germany, officially for violating Belgian neutrality. In fact, Britain was concerned about maintaining its own world power. Now all of the great European powers were at war.

9. What warnings and ultimatums did European countries issue in the summer of 1914? What were the results of these ultimatums?

_____

_____

_____

_____

_____

Reading Essentials and Study Guide

Chapter 8, Section 2

For use with textbook pages 430–437

THE WAR

CONTENT VOCABULARY

propaganda ideas spread to influence public opinion for or against a cause *(page 431)*

trench warfare warfare fought in trenches (ditches protected by barbed war) *(page 431)*

war of attrition a war based on wearing the other side down by constant attacks and heavy losses *(page 432)*

total war a war involving a complete mobilization of resources and people in the warring countries *(page 435)*

planned economies economic systems directed by government agencies *(page 436)*

DRAWING FROM EXPERIENCE

Have you ever read the book *All Quiet on the Western Front?* How does the book describe the fighting on the Western Front during World War I?

In the last section, you learned about the events that led to the start of World War I. In this section, you will learn about the war itself and its impact on civilians at home.

> **California History Social Science Standards**
>
> **10.5** Students analyze the causes and course of the First World War.
>
> **Focuses on:** 10.5.1, 10.5.2

ORGANIZING YOUR THOUGHTS

Use the chart below to help you take notes. World War I was a new kind of war because of new strategies and technology. Indicate how each of the following strategies or technologies was used during the war.

War Strategy or Technology	Use During the War
Propaganda	1.
Trench warfare	2.
War of attrition	3.
Airplanes	4.
Submarines	5.
Planned economies	6.

Reading Essentials and Study Guide

Chapter 8, Section 2 *(continued)*

READ TO LEARN

• 1914 to 1915: Illusions and Stalemate *(page 431)*

Before 1914, many leaders believed that war was so full of risks that it would not be worth fighting. Others believed that diplomats could control any situation and avoid war. In August 1914, these ideas were shown to be wrong.

Prior to the war, government **propaganda** (ideas spread to influence public opinion for or against a cause) had been used to stir up hatred towards other nations. When the war broke out, European governments had no trouble getting their citizens' support for the war effort. Most people were truly convinced that their nation's cause was just. Most people also believed that the war would end in a few weeks.

The German hopes for a quick end to the war rested on a military gamble. The Schlieffen Plan called for German troops to make a wide arc through Belgium into northern France. The German army would then sweep around Paris and surround most of the French army. However, the German advance was halted a short distance from Paris at the First Battle of the Marne (September 6-10). To stop the Germans, the French military leaders loaded 2,000 Parisian taxicabs with fresh troops and sent them to the front.

On this Western Front, the war turned into a stalemate, with both sides taking shelter in their trenches. Trenches were ditches protected by barbed wire. These trenches soon stretched from the English Channel to the border of Switzerland. This **trench warfare** kept both sides in virtually the same positions for four years.

The war on the Eastern Front was fought much differently. There was a great deal of movement by the various armies on this front. As the war began, Russia moved into eastern Germany but was defeated at the Battle of Tannenberg on August 30 and at the Battle of Masurian Lakes on September 15. These defeats ended the Russian threat to Germany. Germany's ally, Austria-Hungary, fared less well at first. The Austrians were defeated by the Russians in Galicia and were thrown out of Serbia. Then Italy, their other ally, betrayed them by attacking Austria in May 1915. Italy joined France, Great Britain, and Russia, who were now called the Allied Powers or Allies.

Germany came to the aid of their Austrian friends. A German-Austrian army defeated the Russians in Galicia and pushed them back into their own territory. The Russians had almost been knocked out of the war. Bulgaria joined Germany and Austria-Hungary in September 1915. They attacked and eliminated Serbia from the war. Their success in the east allowed them to focus their attention back on the Western Front.

Reading Essentials and Study Guide

Chapter 8, Section 2 *(continued)*

7. How did the war on the Western Front turn into a stalemate?

_____

_____

_____

_____

- **1916 to 1917: The Great Slaughter** *(page 432)*

By 1916, the trenches on the Western Front had become elaborate systems of defense. Barbed wire, machine-gun nests, and heavy artillery protected the trenches on both sides. The troops lived in holes in the ground. A strip of land, known as no-man's-land, separated the opposing forces. Trench warfare baffled the military leaders of both sides. Never before in the history of war had armies fought each other in this way. The leaders believed that if they could break through enemy lines, they could return to the type of fighting that they understood. These attempts to break through the lines would begin with a heavy artillery barrage that was intended to flatten the other side's barbed wire and leave them in a state of shock. Troops would then be ordered to leave their trenches and attack the other side with fixed bayonets. These attacks seldom worked, however, because the troops were fired at by the enemy's machine guns. In 1916 and 1917, millions of young men were killed in their attempts to achieve these breakthroughs. World War I had turned into a **war of attrition,** a war based on wearing the other side down by constant attacks and heavy losses.

For the first time in history, warfare was waged in the sky. Airplanes appeared over battlefields for the first time in 1915. At first, planes were only used to spot the enemy's position, but they soon began to attack ground targets. Battles began to be waged between the opposing pilots. At first, they used pistols. Later, machine guns were added to the noses of the planes.

The Germans also used their giant airships, the zeppelins, to bomb London and eastern England. The zeppelins were filled with hydrogen gas, and Germany's enemies soon found that these airships could be turned into raging infernos when hit by antiaircraft guns.

8. Why did attempts to break through enemy lines rarely work under trench warfare?

_____

_____

_____

_____

Reading Essentials and Study Guide

Chapter 8, Section 2 *(continued)*

• Widening of the War *(page 433)*

Because of the stalemate on the Western Front, both sides sought new allies. The Ottoman Empire had already joined the war on Germany's side in August 1914. Russia, Great Britain, and France declared war on the Ottoman Empire in November. The Allies tried to open a Balkan front by landing forces at Gallipoli, southwest of Constantinople, in April 1915. But Bulgaria entered the war on the side of the Central Powers (Germany, Austria-Hungary, and the Ottoman Empire). After a disastrous campaign at Gallipoli, the Allies were forced to withdraw.

By 1917, the war had truly become a world war. Italy, now on the side of the Allies, opened up a front against Austria-Hungary. In the Middle East, a British officer known as Lawrence of Arabia encouraged Arab princes to revolt against their Ottoman rulers. In 1918, British forces from Egypt destroyed the Ottoman Empire in the Middle East. The British used forces from India, Australia, and New Zealand in their Middle East campaigns. During the war, the Allies were able to seize German colonies around the world. Japan, a British ally since 1902, seized several German-held islands in the Pacific. Australia seized German New Guinea.

9. In what ways did the Allies try to widen the war from 1915 to 1918?

_____

_____

_____

_____

_____

• Entry of the United States *(page 434)*

At first, the United States tried to remain neutral. However, as the war dragged on, this became increasingly difficult. The United States finally entered the war as a result of the naval war between Great Britain and Germany. As part of its war strategy, Britain used its navy to block war materials and other goods from reaching Germany by sea. Germany retaliated by setting up its own blockade of Britain. German strategy included the use of submarines. The submarines were allowed to attack not only military ships but also civilian ships, such as passenger liners.

On May 7, 1915, German forces sank the British ship Lusitania. 1,100 civilians were killed, including over 100 Americans. As a result of American protests, the German government <u>suspended</u> unrestricted submarine warfare. The German and British navies fought only one direct battle, the Battle of Jutland. This battle took place on May 31, 1916, and neither side won a conclusive victory.

Academic Vocabulary
suspend: to stop temporarily (p. 435)

Reading Essentials and Study Guide

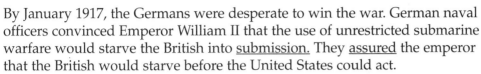

Chapter 8, Section 2 *(continued)*

By January 1917, the Germans were desperate to win the war. German naval officers convinced Emperor William II that the use of unrestricted submarine warfare would starve the British into <u>submission.</u> They <u>assured</u> the emperor that the British would starve before the United States could act.

The German naval officers were wrong. The British did not surrender. The return to unrestricted submarine warfare caused the United States to enter the war in 1917. By 1918, large numbers of American troops had arrived in Europe. The entry of the United States in the war boosted the Allies psychologically and gave them a new source of money and supplies.

10. What was the immediate cause of U.S. entry into World War I?

_____

_____

_____

_____

_____

Academic Vocabulary
submission: an act of yielding to the authority or control of another (p. 435)

Academic Vocabulary
assure: to inform or promise a positive result (p. 435)

• The Home Front: The Impact of Total War *(page 435)*

World War I became a **total war,** a war involving a complete mobilization of resources and people. The war affected all of the citizens in the warring countries. As a result of the war effort, there was an increase in government powers and in the use of propaganda. Once it became clear that the war would last far longer than expected, it also became clear that many more men and supplies would be needed. Governments expanded their powers to meet these needs. Countries drafted tens of millions of young men to serve in their militaries. Wartime governments also expanded their power over their economies. Capitalism, with its free market system, was temporarily set aside. In order to mobilize all the resources of their nations for the war effort, European nations set up **planned economies**—systems directed by government agencies. Governments set up price, wage, and rent controls. They also rationed food supplies and materials, regulated imports and exports, and took over transportation systems and industries.

As the war dragged on and the casualties mounted, patriotic enthusiasm decreased. Wartime governments fought back against the growing opposition to the war. Authoritarian governments, like those of Germany, Russia, and Austria-Hungary, used force to control their people. Soon, even democratic states expanded their police powers in order to stop opposition to the war. In Great Britain, a law was passed that allowed the government to arrest protestors as traitors. Newspapers were censored or even suspended. Governments continued to use propaganda to create enthusiasm for the war.

Because so many of the world's men were involved in fighting the war,

Reading Essentials and Study Guide

Chapter 8, Section 2 *(continued)*

new opportunities were opened up for women. Women were asked to take over jobs that had not been available to them before. But many of the new jobs for women proved to be only temporary when men returned to the job market. There were some lasting results, however. In Germany, Austria, and the United States, women were given the right to vote soon after the war ended. Most British women gained the right to vote by 1918.

11. How did World War I affect the lives of women in Western countries?

_____

_____

_____

_____

_____

Name _____ Date _____ Class _____

Reading Essentials and Study Guide

Chapter 8, Section 3

For use with textbook pages 440–446

THE RUSSIAN REVOLUTION

> ### KEY TERMS
>
> **soviets** councils in Russia composed of representatives from the workers and soldiers *(page 442)*
>
> **war communism** a Communist policy that was used to ensure regular supplies for the Red Army through government control of banks and industries, the seizing of grain from peasants, and the centralization of state administration under Communist control *(page 446)*

DRAWING FROM EXPERIENCE

   What is communism? Have you ever thought what it would be like to live in a Communist country? How would your life be different?

   In the last two sections, you read about World War I. In this section, you will learn about the Russian Revolution, which took place while the war was still going on. By 1921, the Communists were in total command of Russia.

> **California History Social Science Standards**
>
> **10.6** Students analyze the effects of the First World War.
> **10.7** Students analyze the rise of totalitarian governments after the First World War.
>
> **Focuses on:**
> 10.6.2, 10.7.1

ORGANIZING YOUR THOUGHTS

   Use the time line below to help you take notes. Identify eight important events during the Russian Revolution.

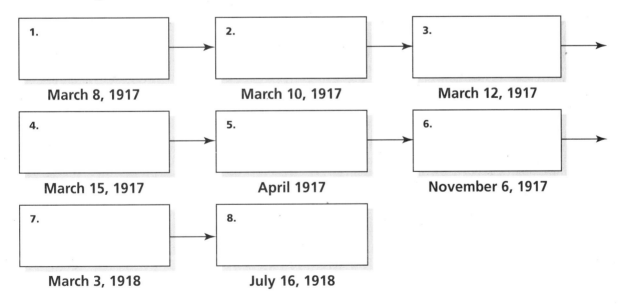

| 1. | 2. | 3. |
| March 8, 1917 | March 10, 1917 | March 12, 1917 |

| 4. | 5. | 6. |
| March 15, 1917 | April 1917 | November 6, 1917 |

| 7. | 8. |
| March 3, 1918 | July 16, 1918 |

Reading Essentials and Study Guide

Chapter 8, Section 3 *(continued)*

READ TO LEARN

- **Background to Revolution** *(page 441)*

Russia was not prepared for World War I. There were no competent military leaders in Russia. Czar Nicholas II was in charge of the armed forces, but he had no training or ability for this. Russian industry was not able to produce the weapons needed for the army. Because of these problems, the Russian army suffered heavy losses. Between 1914 and 1916, two million soldiers were killed.

While the czar was at the battlefront, his wife Alexandra made all of the important decisions. She consulted Rasputin, a Siberian peasant who claimed to be a holy man. She was influenced by him because he seemed to be able to stop the bleeding of her son Alexis, who had hemophilia. Because of his influence, Rasputin became an important power in Russia.

With such poor leadership, the Russian people suffered through a series of military and economic disasters. The people became more and more upset with the rule of the czar. Even the conservative aristocrats, who supported the czar, felt that something must be done. They assassinated Rasputin in December 1916. But even this drastic move could not save the reign of the czar.

In March 1917, working women led a series of strikes in the capital city of Petrograd (formerly St. Petersburg). The government had begun rationing bread. The same women who were working 12-hour days in the factories were now forced to wait in long lines to get bread to feed their children. On March 8, 1917, about 10,000 women marched through the city of Petrograd. Other workers soon joined them. They called for a general strike, which shut down factories in the city on March 10. Czar Nicholas ordered troops to break up the crowds by shooting them if necessary. But large numbers of soldiers soon joined the demonstrators and refused to fire on the crowds.

The Duma, or legislative body, which the czar had tried to dissolve, met anyway. On March 12, it set up a provisional government. This government asked the czar to step down. Because Nicholas II had no support from the army or even from the wealthy aristocrats, he did step down, on March 15. The provisional government, led by Alexander Kerensky, decided to remain in the war to preserve Russia's honor. This was a major blunder. Workers and peasants no longer supported the war. The provisional government was also faced with a challenge to its authority—the **soviets.** The soviets were councils in Russia composed of representatives from the workers and soldiers. They were largely made up of socialists. One group, the Bolsheviks, began to play a crucial role.

Reading Essentials and Study Guide

Chapter 8, Section 3 *(continued)*

9. How did World War I contribute to the start of the Russian Revolution?

_____

_____

_____

_____

• The Rise of Lenin and the Bolsheviks *(page 444)*

The Bolsheviks began as a small faction of a Marxist party called the Russian Social Democrats. Vladimir Ilyich Ulianov, better known as V.I. Lenin, led them. Lenin believed that violent revolution was the only way to destroy the capitalist system. He believed that a small group of well-disciplined revolutionaries could accomplish this. From 1900 to 1917, Lenin spent most of his time abroad. When the provisional government was formed, he saw this as an opportunity for the Bolsheviks to seize power. In April 1917, German military leaders shipped Lenin back to Russia. They hoped that he would create disorder in Russia.

Lenin's arrival started a new stage in the Russian Revolution. He believed that the Bolsheviks should gain control of the soviets and use them to overthrow the provisional government. The Bolsheviks told the people what they wanted to hear. They promised an end to the war, the redistribution of land to the peasants, the transfer of factories from capitalists to the workers, and the transfer of government power to the soviets.

By October 1917, the Bolsheviks held a slight majority in the Petrograd and Moscow soviets. The number of Bolsheviks had grown from 50,000 to 240,000. Leon Trotsky, a dedicated revolutionary, led the Petrograd soviet. This put the Bolsheviks in a position to claim power in the name of the soviets. During the night of November 6, the Bolsheviks seized the Winter Palace, where the provisional government met. The government quickly collapsed. This overthrow coincided with a meeting in Petrograd of the all-Russian Congress of Soviets. This group represented soviets from all over the country. Outwardly, Lenin turned power over to the Congress of Soviets. But the real power passed to the Council of People's Commissars, headed by Lenin.

Academic Vocabulary
coincide: to happen at the same time or place (p. 444)

The Bolsheviks changed their name to the Communists. Now that they were in power, they faced the difficult task of removing Russia from the war. This would mean the loss of much Russian territory, but there was no real choice. On March 3, 1918, Lenin signed the Treaty of Brest-Litovsk and gave up eastern Poland, Ukraine, Finland, and the Baltic provinces. He told his critics the spread of the socialist revolution would make the treaty irrelevant. Even with this treaty, real peace did not come, because the country soon sank into civil war.

Academic Vocabulary
irrelevant: something or someone who is insignificant or unimportant (p. 444)

Reading Essentials and Study Guide

Chapter 16, Section 3 *(continued)*

10. Why did Lenin sign the Treaty of Brest-Litovsk?

_____

_____

_____

_____

- ## Civil War in Russia *(page 444)*

Many people were opposed to the new Communist government. They included groups loyal to the czar, liberals, anti-Lenin socialists, and the Allies. The Allies sent troops to outlying parts of Russia hoping to bring Russia back into the war. The troops rarely fought on Russian soil, but they gave aid to anti-Communist forces. From 1918 to 1921, the Communist (Red) Army was forced to fight on many fronts against the anti-Communist (White) forces. In the early part of the civil war, the White Army had several successes. But by 1920, the major White forces had been defeated. Within a year, the Communists regained control of Ukraine, Georgia, Russian Armenia, and Azerbaijan.

The royal family was a victim of the civil war. On July 16, 1918, members of the local soviet in Ekaterinburg murdered Nicholas II and his family, where they were being held captive.

11. What was the White Army? What groups made it up?

_____

_____

_____

_____

Reading Essentials and Study Guide

Chapter 8, Section 3 *(continued)*

• Triumph of the Communists *(page 445)*

The Communists had won the civil war over so many opponents. There were several reasons for their success. First, the Red Army was well disciplined. This was largely due to the efforts of Leon Trotsky, the commissar of war. He reinstated the draft and insisted on complete obedience. Second, the Whites were not unified. They had no common goal, and the different groups did not trust each other. The Communists, on the other hand, had a clear vision of a new socialist order. Third, the Communists implemented a policy of **war communism.** This policy was used to ensure regular supplies for the Red Army. This meant government control of banks and industries, the seizing of grain from peasants, and the centralization of state administration under Communist control. The Communists also formed a new secret police, known as the Cheka. The Cheka began a Red Terror aimed at destroying those who opposed the new regime. Finally, the presence of foreign armies on Russian soil was used to stir up Russian patriotism. The Communists were able to call on patriotic Russians to fight foreign attempts to control the country.

By 1921, the Communists had total control of Russia. Russia was now a centralized state dominated by a single party. The state was also hostile to the Allies, because the Allies had helped the Communists' enemies in the civil war.

12. Why did the Communists win the civil war in Russia?

_____

_____

_____

_____

_____

Reading Essentials and Study Guide

Chapter 8, Section 4

For use with textbook pages 447–453

END OF THE WAR

CONTENT VOCABULARY

armistice a truce or an agreement to end the fighting in a war *(page 449)*

reparation a payment by a nation defeated in a war to other nations to cover the costs of the war *(page 450)*

mandate a commission from the League of Nations to a nation that allowed it to officially govern another nation or region without actually owning the territory *(page 452)*

DRAWING FROM EXPERIENCE

Have you ever heard the slogans, "the war to end all wars" and "to make the world safe for democracy"? Did you know that these slogans were used in reference to World War I?

In the last section, you read about the events that led to the Russian Revolution. In this section, you will read about the end of World War I and the efforts to restore peace after the war.

> **California History Social Science Standards**
>
> **10.5** Students analyze the causes and course of the First World War. **10.6** Students analyze the effects of the First World War.
>
> **Focuses on:** 10.5.2, 10.5.3, 10.6.1, 10.6.2, 10.6.3

ORGANIZING YOUR THOUGHTS

Use the chart below to help you take notes. In January 1919, representatives of the victorious nations met in Paris to make a final settlement of World War I. The peace settlement with Germany was called the Treaty of Versailles. List the major provisions of the treaty as they relate to the four areas in this chart.

Major Provisions of the Treaty of Versailles	
Responsibility/costs of the war	1.
Military	2.
Territory	3.
Buffer zone	4.

Reading Essentials and Study Guide

Chapter 8, Section 4 *(continued)*

READ TO LEARN

- ## The Last Year of the War *(page 448)*

1917 had been a very difficult year for the Allied forces. Their offensives on the Western Front had been defeated, and the Russian Revolution led to Russia's withdrawal from the War. However, the entry of the United States into the war gave the Allies a much-needed psychological boost. In 1918, fresh American troops would be crucial.

With Russia out of the war, Germany was free to <u>concentrate</u> entirely on the Western Front. Erich von Ludendorff, who guided German military operations, decided to make a grand offensive to break the stalemate. The German attack began in March 1918. The Germans were stopped at the Second Battle of the Marne on July 18. French, Moroccan, and American forces, supported by hundreds of tanks, threw the Germans back over the Marne. The German offensive had failed.

Academic Vocabulary
concentrate: to focus all attention on something or someone (p. 448)

With more than a million American troops pouring into France, the Allies began to advance toward Germany. On September 29, 1918, General Ludendorff informed the German leaders that the war was lost. He demanded that the government ask for peace. The Allies were unwilling to make peace with the present German government, so reforms were begun to create a more liberal government. However, the exhausted German people were unwilling to wait for this process to take place. On November 3, sailors in the town of Kiel mutinied. Soldiers and workers began to form councils throughout Germany. By November 9, William II was forced to leave the country. The Social Democrats under Friedrich Ebert announced the creation of a democratic republic. On November 11, the new government signed an **armistice** (a truce or an agreement to end the fighting in a war).

The war was over, but revolutionary forces had been set in motion in Germany. A group of radical socialists formed the German Communist Party in December 1918. The Communists tried to seize power in both Berlin and Munich. The new Social Democratic government used army troops to crush the rebels and murdered two of the Communist party leaders. The attempt at revolution left the German middle class with a deep fear of communism.

Austria-Hungary also experienced revolution. Ethnic groups tried harder and harder to gain their independence. By the end of the war, the Austro-Hungarian Empire no longer existed. The independent republics of Austria, Hungary, and Czechoslovakia, along with the monarchical state called Yugoslavia, replaced it.

Reading Essentials and Study Guide

Chapter 8, Section 4 *(continued)*

5. What was the effect of the U.S. entry into World War I?

_____

_____

_____

_____

_____

• **The Peace Settlements** *(page 449)*

In January 1919, representatives of 27 victorious Allied nations met in Paris to make a final settlement of the war. Idealistic reasons for fighting World War I had replaced the original reasons for starting the war. Even before the war ended, the U.S. president, Woodrow Wilson, had presented his "Fourteen Points" to the U.S. Congress. These points were his basis for a peace settlement. His proposals included reaching the peace agreements openly rather than through secret diplomacy, reducing armaments (military forces) to a "point <u>consistent</u> with domestic safety," and ensuring self-determination (the right of each people to have its own nation). He also pushed for a general association of nations that would guarantee independence for large and small nations alike.

> **Academic Vocabulary**
>
> **consistent:** marked by harmony, regularity, or steady continuity; free from variation or contradiction (p. 449)

When the delegations met at the Paris Peace Conference, it became obvious that secret treaties and agreements had been made before the war. These agreements had raised the hopes of European nations for territorial gains. These hopes could not be totally ignored, even if they were in conflict with the principle of self-determination. David Lloyd George, prime minister of Great Britain, was determined to make Germany pay for the war. Georges Clemenceau, the premier of France, was mainly concerned about national security. Clemenceau wanted Germany to be stripped of all weapons. He also wanted German **reparations** (payments to cover the costs of the war) and a separate Rhineland as a buffer zone between France and Germany.

Wilson, Lloyd George, and Clemenceau made the most important decisions at the Paris Peace Conference. Germany was not even invited to attend, and Russia could not be present because of civil war. On January 25, 1919, the conference accepted Wilson's idea of a League of Nations. In return, Wilson agreed to make compromises on territorial arrangements. He did this because he believed that the League could later fix any unfair arrangements. Clemenceau also compromised. He gave up France's wish for a separate Rhineland.

The final peace settlement consisted of five separate treaties with the defeated nations (Germany, Austria, Hungary, Bulgaria, and Turkey). The most important treaty was the Treaty of Versailles with Germany. It was signed on June 28, 1919. The War Guilt <u>Clause</u> said that Germany and

> **Academic Vocabulary**
>
> **clause:** a distinct article in a formal document (p. 451)

Reading Essentials and Study Guide

Chapter 8, Section 4 (continued)

Austria were responsible for starting the war. It ordered Germany to pay reparations for the damage done to the Allied nations. Germany also had to reduce its army and navy and eliminate its air force. Alsace and Lorraine were returned to France. Parts of eastern Germany were given to a new Polish state. German land on both sides of the Rhine was made a demilitarized zone and stripped of all weapons and fortifications. It was hoped that this would prevent Germany from making advances toward France.

As a result of the war and the peace treaties, the map of Europe was redrawn. Both the German and Russian empires lost much territory. The Austro-Hungarian Empire disappeared. New nations emerged: Finland, Latvia, Estonia, Lithuania, Poland, Czechoslovakia, Austria, and Hungary. Romania acquired additional lands from Russia, Hungary, and Bulgaria. Serbia became part of a new nation, called Yugoslavia. The Paris Peace Conference was supposedly guided by the principle of self-determination, but the mixtures of peoples in Eastern Europe made it impossible to draw boundaries totally along ethnic lines. As a result, almost every eastern European country still had ethnic minorities. The problem of ethnic minorities would lead to later conflicts.

The Ottoman Empire was also broken up by the peace settlement. To gain Arab support during the war, the Allies had promised to recognize the independence of Arab states in the Ottoman Empire. After the war, however, France took control of Lebanon and Syria, and Britain took control of Iraq and Palestine. These arrangements were called **mandates**. Under the mandate system, a nation officially governed another nation as a mandate from the League of Nations but did not own the territory.

World War I had other results as well. The death of so many people undermined the idea of progress. This war had been a total war that required a complete mobilization of people and resources. The power of governments increased. The turmoil created by the war led to even more insecurity. Revolutions broke up old empires. New states were created, which led to new problems.

6. What new nations emerged as a result of the war and the peace treaties?

_____

_____

_____

_____

_____

Reading Essentials and Study Guide

Chapter 9, Section 1

For use with textbook pages 463–469

THE FUTILE SEARCH FOR STABILITY

CONTENT VOCABULARY

depression   a period of low economic activity and rising unemployment *(page 466)*

collective bargaining   the right of unions to negotiate with employers over wages and hours *(page 468)*

deficit spending   going into debt to finance government projects *(page 469)*

DRAWING FROM EXPERIENCE

Have you ever read the novel *The Grapes of Wrath*? Have you ever seen the film? What period in history is portrayed in this novel?

In this section, you will learn about events in Europe and the United States following World War I. After a brief period of peace and prosperity, the Western nations were shaken by the Great Depression.

California History Social Science Standards

10.6 Students analyze the effects of the First World War.
10.8 Students analyze the causes and consequences of World War II.

Focuses on:
10.6.1, 10.6.2, 10.6.3, 10.8.2

ORGANIZING YOUR THOUGHTS

Use the diagram below to help you take notes. Identify two causes and three political effects of the Great Depression.

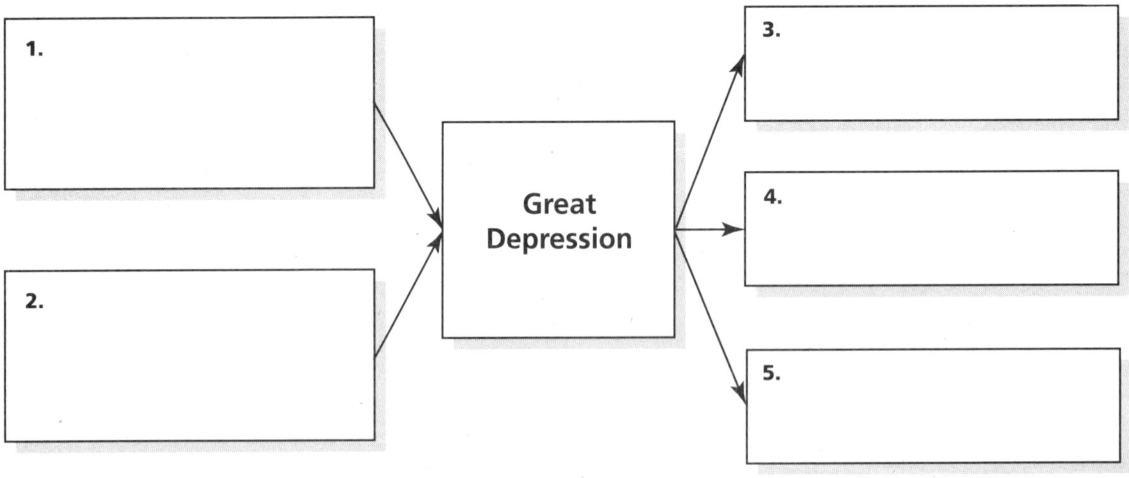

1. _____

2. _____

Great Depression

3. _____

4. _____

5. _____

Reading Essentials and Study Guide

Chapter 9, Section 1 *(continued)*

READ TO LEARN

• Uneasy Peace, Uncertain Security *(page 464)*

The peace settlement at the end of World War I made many nations unhappy. Some of the provisions in the settlement led to border disputes in eastern Europe. The League of Nations was not very effective in maintaining peace. This was partly because the League could not agree to use military force against aggression. It was also due to the fact that the United States was not in the League. The U.S. Senate refused to ratify (approve) the Treaty of Versailles. This meant that the United States could not be a member of the League of Nations.

The Germans, in particular, were unhappy with the peace settlement. The French government demanded strict enforcement of the Treaty of Versailles. In April 1921, the Allied Reparations Commission determined that Germany had to pay 33 billion dollars for reparations (the payments Germany was required to make for war damages). Germany tried to make these payments, but after one year, they announced that they could no longer afford to pay. France sent troops to occupy the Ruhr Valley, the chief industrial and mining center of Germany. The French intended to collect reparations by operating the Ruhr mines and factories. German workers resisted by going on strike. To pay the workers, the German government printed more and more paper money. This added to the inflation (rise in prices) that had already begun in Germany. The German mark (Germany's currency) soon became worthless. Workers took their weekly pay home in wheelbarrows.

The Allies could see that this situation could not continue. In August 1924, a new plan for reparations, the Dawes Plan, was produced. It reduced the total amount that Germany had to pay. It also reduced the yearly payment amount to something that Germany could afford to pay. The plan also granted a $200 million loan to Germany. This loan opened the door to American investments in Europe. There was a brief period of prosperity from 1924 to 1929.

In 1925, France and Germany signed the Treaty of Locarno. This treaty guaranteed Germany's new western borders. This treaty was viewed by many as the beginning of a new era of European peace. Germany joined the League of Nations in 1926. In 1928, sixty-three nations signed the Kellogg-Briand pact. These nations pledged "to renounce war as an instrument of national policy." Unfortunately, there was no way to enforce the Kellogg-Briand pact. Most nations were unwilling to risk their national security by reducing their military forces.

Reading Essentials and Study Guide

Chapter 9, Section 1 *(continued)*

6. Why was the League of Nations not very effective in maintaining peace?

_____

_____

_____

_____

- ## The Great Depression *(page 466)*

The brief period of prosperity that began in 1924 ended in an economic collapse that became known as the Great Depression. A **depression** is a period of low economic activity and rising unemployment.

At least two factors played an important role in the start of the Great Depression. The first factor was a series of downturns in the economies of individual nations during the second half of the 1920s. The second factor was an international financial crisis involving the U.S. stock market. During the 1920s, the United States stock market was booming. American investors, who had been making loans to Germany, began to pull money out of Germany to invest it in the stock market. Then, in October 1929, the stock market crashed. American investors withdrew even more money from Germany and other European markets. This weakened the banks of Germany and other European countries. By 1931, trade was slowing down, industrial production was declining, and unemployment was rising. During 1932, the worst year of the depression, 25 percent of British workers were unemployed, and 40 percent of the German workforce was without work. Governments did not know how to deal with the crisis. Traditional solutions, such as cutting costs by lowering wages, made matters worse.

The Great Depression had serious political effects. First, governments became more and more involved in the economies of their countries. Second, Communism became more popular. Marx had predicted that capitalism would eventually destroy itself through overproduction, and this seemed to be coming true. Finally, masses of people began to follow dictators who offered solutions.

7. How did the crash of the U.S. stock market affect Germany and other European countries?

_____

_____

_____

_____

Reading Essentials and Study Guide

Chapter 9, Section 1 (continued)

• Democratic States After the War (page 467)

In 1919, most European countries had democratic governments. In many nations, women could now vote. In Germany, the imperial government had come to an end. A German democratic state known as the Weimar Republic was created, but it had problems. First, it had no outstanding political leaders. In 1925, Paul von Hindenburg was elected president. He was a military hero and did not fully endorse the republic that he was elected to lead. The Weimar Republic also had serious economic problems. Inflation caused fixed incomes and life savings to become worthless. This pushed the middle class toward political parties that opposed the republic. After a brief period of prosperity, the Great Depression struck and led to mass unemployment. Fear seized the country and led to the rise of extremist parties.

After the war, France was the strongest European power. Because its economy was more balanced than the economies of other nations, the French did not experience the full effects of the Great Depression until 1932. The economic problems had political effects. The government changed six times in less than two years. Finally, in 1936, a coalition of leftist parties (Communists, Socialists, and Radicals) formed the Popular Front government. This government gave workers the right to **collective bargaining,** (the right of unions to negotiate with employers over wages and hours), a 40-hour workweek, a two-week paid vacation, and a <u>minimum</u> wage. But the Popular Front's policies were unable to solve the problems of the depression.

Academic Vocabulary
minimum: the lowest amount possible (p. 469)

During the war, Great Britain had lost many of the markets for its products to the United States and Japan. This led to a rise in unemployment. From 1925 to 1929, however, Britain had a period of prosperity. After the Great Depression struck, the Labour Party was unable to solve the country's problems and fell from power in 1931. A new government, led by the Conservatives, took credit for bringing Britain out of the worst stages of the depression.

Most of the political leaders in Britain ignored the new ideas of a British economist, John Maynard Keynes. Keynes believed that unemployment came from a decline in demand, not from overproduction. He believed that the government should increase demand by putting people back to work building highways and public buildings. He believed that governments should finance these projects even if this meant **deficit spending** (going into debt).

After Germany, no nation was more affected by the Great Depression than the United States. By 1933, over 12 million people were unemployed. Under these <u>circumstances</u>, Franklin Delano Roosevelt was elected to the presidency in 1932. He introduced an economic policy called the New Deal. The New Deal included an increased program of public works. The Roosevelt administration also introduced new legislation that began the U.S. welfare system. In 1935, the Social Security Act created old-age pensions and unemployment

Academic Vocabulary
circumstance: a condition, fact, or event accompanying, conditioning, or determining another (p. 469)

Reading Essentials and Study Guide

Chapter 9, Section 1 (continued)

insurance. However, the New Deal alone could not solve the unemployment problems of the Great Depression. In 1938, more than 10 million Americans were still unemployed.

8. What was the New Deal?

_____

_____

_____

_____

_____

_____

Reading Essentials and Study Guide

Chapter 9, Section 2

For use with textbook pages 470–477

THE RISE OF DICTATORIAL REGIMES

CONTENT VOCABULARY

totalitarian state   a government that aims to control the political, economic, social, intellectual, and cultural lives of its citizens *(page 471)*

fascism   a political philosophy that glorifies the state above the individual by emphasizing the need for a strong central government led by a dictatorial ruler *(page 471)*

New Economic Policy   an economic policy in Russia under Lenin that was a modified version of the old capitalist system *(page 474)*

Politburo   a seven-member committee that was the leading policy-making body of the Communist Party in the Soviet Union *(page 474)*

collectivization   a system in which private farms are eliminated in favor of government owner-ship of the land *(page 475)*

DRAWING FROM EXPERIENCE

What do you think of when you hear the word "fascist"? Why do people follow fascist leaders?

In the last section, you read about economic problems in Europe and the United States following World War I. In this section, you will learn how dictators came to power in several countries during this period. The economic problems in these countries were a major factor in the rise of these dictatorships.

ORGANIZING YOUR THOUGHTS

Use the chart below to help you take notes. List the dictator who took control in each of these countries following World War I, and describe how each dictator came to power.

California History Social Science Standards

10.6 Students analyze the effects of the First World War.
10.7 Students analyze the rise of totalitarian governments after the First World War.
10.8 Students analyze the causes and consequences of World War II.

Focuses on:
10.6.3, 10.7.1, 10.7.2, 10.7.3, 10.8.1, 10.8.5

Country	Dictator	How He Came to Power
Italy	1.	2.
Soviet Union	3.	4.
Spain	5.	6.

Reading Essentials and Study Guide

Chapter 9, Section 2 (continued)

READ TO LEARN

• The Rise of Dictators (page 471)

The apparent triumph of democracy in Europe in 1919 was extremely short-lived. Of the major European powers, only France and Great Britain were still democratic by 1939. Italy, the Soviet Union, Germany, and many other European countries adopted dictatorships. Some of these dictatorships were totalitarian states. A **totalitarian state** is a government that aims to control the political, economic, social, intellectual, and cultural lives of its citizens. These totalitarian states wanted to control the minds and the hearts of their citizens. This goal was achieved through the use of mass propaganda techniques and modern communications. A single leader and a single party led the totalitarian states. The result was government that was no longer interested in individual freedoms but in imposing the collective will of the masses on everyone. Of course, the will of the masses was determined and organized by the dictator.

7. What is a totalitarian state?

_____

_____

_____

_____

• Fascism in Italy (page 471)

In the early 1920s, Benito Mussolini established the first European Fascist movement in Italy. **Fascism** is a political philosophy that glorifies the state above the individual by emphasizing the need for a strong central government led by a dictator. The government controls people, and any opposition is suppressed.

Italy, like other European countries, experienced severe economic problems following World War I. Inflation grew, and there were strikes. Socialists spoke of revolution. The middle class was afraid of a Communist takeover. In 1919, from this background of <u>widespread</u> unrest, Mussolini created a new political group, the *Fascio di Combattimento* (League of Combat). The term fascist comes from this name. In 1920 and 1921, he formed bands of armed Fascists called *squadristi* (Blackshirts). They attacked socialist offices and newspapers. They also used violence to break up strikes. By 1922, Mussolini's movement was growing rapidly. The middle-class fear of socialism, communism, and disorder made the Fascists attractive to many people. Mussolini also knew that the Italian people were angry that Italy did not receive more land in the peace settlement after the war. He won thousands of supporters by demanding more land.

Academic Vocabulary
widespread: a belief or event that is common almost everywhere (p. 472)

146

Reading Essentials and Study Guide

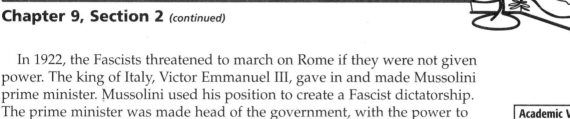

Chapter 9, Section 2 *(continued)*

In 1922, the Fascists threatened to march on Rome if they were not given power. The king of Italy, Victor Emmanuel III, gave in and made Mussolini prime minister. Mussolini used his position to create a Fascist dictatorship. The prime minister was made head of the government, with the power to make laws by decree. The police were given <u>unrestricted</u> power to arrest and jail people. In 1926, the Fascists outlawed all other political parties in Italy. Mussolini ruled Italy as *Il Duce,* "The Leader."

> **Academic Vocabulary**
>
> **unrestricted:** to have power without limits or restrictions (p. 472)

Mussolini used various means to control the Italian people. He created a secret police, known as the OVRA. He also used the mass media to spread propaganda. The Fascists used organizations to promote fascism and to control the people. For example, youth groups were formed that focused on military activities and values. The Fascists hoped to create a nation of new Italians who were fit, disciplined, and war-loving.

However, the Fascists did not completely destroy the country's old power structure. The military was able to keep most of its independence. Victor Emmanuel was retained as king. The Catholic Church was allowed to keep its territory in Rome, known as Vatican City. Mussolini also gave the Church a large grant of money and recognized Catholicism as the "sole religion of the state." In return, the Catholic Church recognized the Italian state and encouraged Italians to support the Fascist regime.

8. What is fascism?

_____

_____

_____

_____

• A New Era in the Soviet Union *(page 473)*

During the civil war in Russia, Lenin followed a policy of war communism. The government controlled most industries and took grain from peasants in order to feed the army. When the war was over, peasants began to sabotage the program by hoarding food. The situation became even worse when a great famine hit Russia between 1920 and 1922. Five million people died. Industrial collapse followed the famine.

In March 1921, Lenin gave up the policy of war communism. He began a program known as the **New Economic Policy** (NEP). It was a modified version of the old capitalist system. Peasants were allowed to sell their produce openly. Small businesses could be privately owned and operated. The NEP saved the country from economic disaster. In 1922, Lenin and the Communists formally created a new state called the Union of Soviet Socialist Republics (also known as the USSR or the Soviet Union.)

Reading Essentials and Study Guide

Chapter 9, Section 2 (continued)

When Lenin died in 1924, there was a struggle for power within the Politburo. The **Politburo** was a seven-member committee that had become the leading policy-making body of the Communist Party. One group in the Politburo wanted to end the NEP and begin a program of rapid industrialization. Leon Trotsky led this group. This group also wanted to spread communism to other nations around the world. Another group wanted to continue the NEP and to focus on building a socialist state in Russia. This group believed that rapid industrialization would hurt the peasants.

At the same time, there was a personal rivalry in the Politburo between Trotsky and another Politburo member, Joseph Stalin. Stalin was the party general secretary and appointed regional and local party officials. He used this influential position to gain control of the Communist Party. Because he had appointed thousands of officials within the party, he had a great deal of support. By 1929, Stalin was able to establish a powerful dictatorship. Trotsky was expelled from the party and eventually murdered.

The Stalinist era was a period of economic, social and political changes that were even more revolutionary than the revolutions of 1917. Stalin ended the NEP in 1928 and began his first Five-Year Plan. The Five-Year Plans set economic goals for five-year periods. Their purpose was to transform Russia from an agricultural country into an industrial country. The First Five-Year Plan emphasized the production of capital equipment (heavy machines that produce other goods) and weapons. This plan resulted in dramatic increases in the production of steel and oil. But the Russian people paid a terrible price for industrialization. The number of workers in the cities increased by millions, but housing actually declined. As a result, millions of people lived in pitiful conditions. Wages also declined by 43 percent between 1928 and 1940. The government also began to collectivize farms. **Collectivization** was a system in which private farms were eliminated. Instead, the government owned all of the land while the peasants worked it. By 1934, 26 million family farms had been collectivized into 250,000 units. Like industrialization, collectivization had a terrible cost. Peasants responded by hoarding food and killing livestock. This produced a widespread famine. 10 million peasants died in famines in 1932 and 1933.

Stalin's programs had other costs. Stalin's mania for power led him to purge (remove) all of his opponents. First, he removed the Old Bolsheviks (people who had been involved in the early days of the revolution). Stalin also purged army officials, diplomats, union officials, party members, intellectuals, and many ordinary citizens. Eight million Russians were arrested. Millions were sent to labor camps in Siberia. Others were executed.

Reading Essentials and Study Guide

Chapter 9, Section 2 *(continued)*

9. What economic changes were made during the Stalinist Era?

_____

_____

_____

_____

• Authoritarian States in the West *(page 476)*

Some governments in the West were not totalitarian but authoritarian. They had some features in common with totalitarian states, such as using police powers. But these governments did not try to create a new kind of mass society. Their main concern was preserving the old social order.

Authoritarian governments developed in some of the new nations in Eastern Europe. Austria, Poland, Czechoslovakia, Yugoslavia, Romania, Bulgaria, and Hungary all adopted parliamentary systems after the war. But authoritarian governments soon replaced most of these systems. Only Czechoslovakia maintained its democracy. Parliamentary systems failed for several reasons. First, these countries did not have a tradition of democracy. They were mostly rural, and many of the peasants were illiterate. Ethnic conflicts also caused problems. Powerful landowners, the churches, and even some members of the middle class were afraid of land reform, communism, and ethnic conflict. These groups supported authoritarian governments that maintained the old system.

In Spain, democracy also failed to survive. General Francisco Franco led a revolt against the democratic government in 1936. A bloody civil war began. Germany and Italy aided Franco's forces with weapons, money, and men. The Spanish republican government was aided by thousands of foreign volunteers and by trucks, planes, tanks, and advisers from the Soviet Union. The Spanish Civil War ended when Franco's forces took Madrid in 1939. Franco established a dictatorship that favored large landowners, businesspeople, and the Catholic clergy. Because it favored traditional groups and did not try to control every aspect of people's lives, his dictatorship was authoritarian, not totalitarian.

10. Why did parliamentary systems fail in many Eastern European countries?

_____

_____

_____

_____

Reading Essentials and Study Guide

Chapter 9, Section 3

For use with textbook pages 478–483

HITLER AND NAZI GERMANY

CONTENT VOCABULARY
Reichstag   the German parliament *(page 480)*
concentration camp   large prison camps in which members of minority groups and political dissidents are confined *(page 481)*

DRAWING FROM EXPERIENCE

Have you ever read *The Diary of Anne Frank?* What does Anne Frank describe in her diary?

In the last section, you read about the rise of dictatorial regimes in several countries in Europe. In this section, you will read about the rise of Hitler and the Nazi party in Germany.

California History Social Science Standards

10.7 Students analyze the rise of totalitarian governments after the First World War.
10.8 Students analyze the causes and consequences of World War II.
Focuses on:
10.7.3, 10.8.1, 10.8.5

ORGANIZING YOUR THOUGHTS

Use the chart below to help you take notes. Summarize the policies and activities of Hitler and the Nazi Party as they relate to the subjects or groups in this chart.

Nazi Policies and Activities	
Terror	1.
Economy	2.
Spectacles/organizations	3.
Women	4.
Jews	5.

Glencoe World History—Modern Times

Reading Essentials and Study Guide

Chapter 9, Section 3 *(continued)*

READ TO LEARN

• Hitler and His Views *(page 479)*

Adolf Hitler was born in Austria in 1889. He moved to Vienna to become an artist but was rejected by the Vienna <u>Academy</u> of Fine Arts. While in Vienna, however, he developed his basic ideas. Racism was at the center of Hitler's ideas. Hitler was also an extreme nationalist. He believed in the need for struggle. In 1919, he joined the German Worker's Party, a right-wing extreme nationalist party in Munich. By the summer of 1921, Hitler had taken total control of the party. He renamed it the National Socialist German Workers' Party (NSDAP) or Nazi for short.

In 1923, he organized an armed uprising against the government in Munich. This uprising, called the Beer Hall Putsch, was crushed, and Hitler was put in prison. During his time in prison, Hitler wrote *Mein Kampf*, a book about his movement and its basic ideas. In *Mein Kampf*, extreme German nationalism, strong anti-Semitism, and anticommunism are combined with a theory of struggle. Hitler's theory emphasized the right of superior nations to gain *Lebensraum* (living space) through expansion. It also emphasized the right of superior individuals to gain authoritarian leadership over the masses.

Academic Vocabulary
academy: a high school or college where special subjects or skills are taught (p. 480)

6. What were some of the ideas expressed by Hitler in *Mein Kampf?*

_____

_____

_____

_____

_____

• Rise of Nazism *(page 479)*

Hitler decided that the Nazis would have to gain power by legal means, not by a violent overthrow of the government. This meant that the Nazi Party would have to become a mass political party that could compete for votes. After his release from prison, Hitler expanded the Nazi Party to all parts of Germany. By 1932, it had 800,000 members and was the largest party in the **Reichstag** (the German parliament).

Germany's economic problems were a crucial factor in the Nazi rise to power. Unemployment had risen to 6 million by the winter of 1932. The impact of the Great Depression made extremist parties more attractive. Hitler also promised to create a new Germany. His focus on national pride, national honor, and traditional militarism appealed to his listeners.

Reading Essentials and Study Guide

Chapter 9, Section 3 *(continued)*

7. How did the Great Depression contribute to the rise of Nazism in Germany?

_____

_____

_____

• Victory of Nazism *(page 480)*

The elites of Germany looked to Hitler for leadership. He had the mass support to create a right-wing, authoritarian government that would save Germany and people in privileged positions from a Communist takeover. In 1933, President Hindenburg agreed to allow Hitler to become chancellor and create a new government. On March 23, 1933, the Reichstag passed the Enabling Act. This law gave the government the power to ignore the constitution for four years while it issued laws to deal with the country's problems. It gave Hitler's actions a legal basis. He no longer needed the Reichstag or President Hindenburg. He became a dictator appointed by the Reichstag itself.

The Nazis worked quickly to bring all institutions under Nazi control. The civil service was purged of Jews and democratic elements. Large prison camps (called **concentration camps**) were set up for people who opposed the new government. Trade unions were dissolved. All political parties except for the Nazis were abolished. When Hindenburg died in 1934, the office of president was also abolished. Hitler became the sole ruler of Germany. Public officials and soldiers were required to take an oath of loyalty to Hitler as their *Führer* ("Leader").

8. What was the Enabling Act?

_____

_____

_____

• The Nazi State, 1933–1939 *(page 481)*

Hitler wanted to develop a state that reflected his ideas about a pure "Aryan" race. Nazis thought that the Germans were the true descendants of the Aryans. (They misused the term Aryan to mean the ancient Greeks and Romans and twentieth-century Germans and Scandinavians.) They believed that there had been two German empires or *Reichs* (the Holy Roman Empire and the German Empire of 1871 to 1918). It was Hitler's goal to create a Third Reich, the empire of Nazi Germany, to dominate Europe for generations to come. In this empire, every activity of the individual would be controlled by the Nazi party, and there would be no "arbitrary will."

Reading Essentials and Study Guide

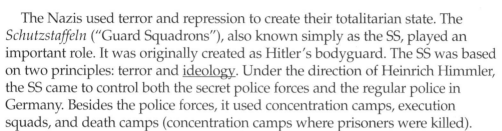

Chapter 9, Section 3 *(continued)*

The Nazis used terror and repression to create their totalitarian state. The *Schutzstaffeln* ("Guard Squadrons"), also known simply as the SS, played an important role. It was originally created as Hitler's bodyguard. The SS was based on two principles: terror and <u>ideology</u>. Under the direction of Heinrich Himmler, the SS came to control both the secret police forces and the regular police in Germany. Besides the police forces, it used concentration camps, execution squads, and death camps (concentration camps where prisoners were killed).

> **Academic Vocabulary**
>
> **ideology:** a systematic body of ideas, especially about human life or culture (p. 482)

To end the depression, Hitler created public works projects and gave money to construction firms to put people back to work. But it was a huge rearmament program that finally solved the unemployment problem. By 1937, less than 500,000 people were unemployed. The Nazis' part in bringing an end to the depression was an important reason that many Germans accepted Hitler and the Nazis. Demonstrations and spectacles were also used to make the German people accept Hitler's policies. These events created mass enthusiasm and excitement. Churches, schools, and universities were also brought under the control of the Nazis. Youth organizations were created that taught Nazi ideals.

Women were considered important in the Aryan state because they bore children. The Nazis believed that men were meant to be warriors and political leaders, while women were meant to be wives and mothers. These ideas determined employment opportunities for women. Jobs in heavy industry, university teaching, medicine, and law were considered unsuitable for women. The Nazis encouraged women to pursue other occupations, such as social work and nursing, or not to work at all.

The Nazi party reflected Hitler's anti-Semitic beliefs. In September 1935, the Nazis announced new racial laws at the annual party rally in Nuremburg. These "Nuremburg Laws" excluded Jews from German citizenship and forbade marriages between Jews and German citizens. Jews were also required to wear yellow Stars of David and to carry identification cards saying they were Jewish. A more violent phase of anti-Semitism began on the night of November 9, 1938—*Kristallnacht* ("the night of shattered glass"). Nazis burned synagogues and destroyed seven thousand Jewish businesses. Thirty thousand Jewish men were rounded up and sent to concentration camps. At least a hundred Jews were killed. After *Kristallnacht,* Jews were barred from all public transportation and public buildings, such as schools and hospitals. They were not allowed to own, manage, or work in any retail store. Jews were also encouraged to emigrate from Germany.

9. What did the Nazis mean when they used the term *Aryan?*

_____

_____

_____

Reading Essentials and Study Guide

Chapter 9, Section 4

For use with textbook pages 486–491

CULTURAL AND INTELLECTUAL TRENDS

CONTENT VOCABULARY

photomontage   a picture made of a combination of photographs *(page 489)*

surrealism   artistic movement that seeks to depict the world of the unconscious *(page 489)*

uncertainty principle   a theory of the German physicist Werner Heisenberg that suggests that all physical laws governing the universe are based in uncertainty *(page 491)*

DRAWING FROM EXPERIENCE

What do you like to do with your free time? Do you go to movies and sporting events? Or do you spend most of your free time at home?

In the last three sections, you learned about economic problems and political developments in Western countries after the end of World War I. In this section, you will learn about cultural and intellectual developments during this time. New work patterns after World War I provided people with more free time to pursue leisure activities.

ORGANIZING YOUR THOUGHTS

Use the diagram below to help you take notes. The years following World War I were characterized by political, economic, and social uncertainty. Describe how this uncertainty was reflected in art, literature, and science.

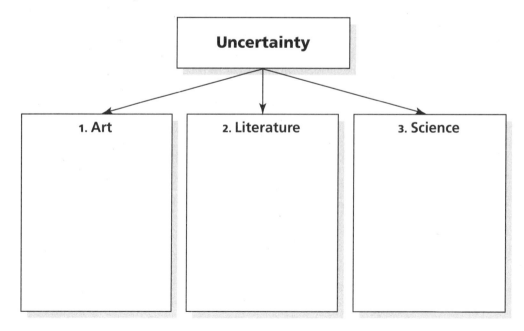

Reading Essentials and Study Guide

Chapter 9, Section 4 (continued)

READ TO LEARN

• Mass Culture: Radio and Movies (page 487)

A series of inventions in the late nineteenth century led to a revolution in mass communications. After Marconi's discovery of wireless radio waves, broadcasting facilities were built in the United States, Europe, and Japan in 1921 and 1922. Mass production of radios also began. Although motion pictures had first appeared in the 1890s, full-length feature films did not appear until shortly after World War I. By 1939, about 40 percent of adults in the more industrialized countries were attending a movie once a week.

Radio and the movies were used for political purposes. Radio enabled leaders like Hitler to get their messages to the masses. The Nazi regime encouraged manufacturers to produce inexpensive radios that could be bought on an installment plan. Movies also had propaganda potential. Joseph Goebbels, the propaganda minister of Nazi Germany, created a special film division in his Propaganda Ministry. It supported the making of both documentaries (nonfiction films) and popular feature films that carried the Nazi message.

4. How were radio and the movies used for political purposes in Nazi Germany?

_____

_____

_____

_____

• Mass Leisure (page 488)

By 1920, the eight-hour workday had been established for many workers in Europe. This gave people more free time for leisure activities. Leisure activities included professional sporting events and travel. Trains, buses, and cars made trips to the beach or holiday resorts popular and affordable. Mass leisure also offered new ways for totalitarian states to control the people. The Nazis adopted a program called *Kraft durch Freude* ("Strength through Joy"). The program offered its own leisure activities, including concerts, operas, films, guided tours, and sporting events. The program's inexpensive vacations were especially popular.

5. How did the Nazis use leisure activities to control people?

_____

_____

_____

Reading Essentials and Study Guide

Chapter 9, Section 4 *(continued)*

• Artistic and Literary Trends *(page 488)*

World War I had left many Europeans with a sense of despair. To many people, the war meant that something was terribly wrong with Western values and that human beings were violent animals who were <u>incapable</u> of creating a sane and rational world. The Great Depression and the growth of fascist movements added to the despair and uncertainty. This uncertainty was reflected in the artistic and intellectual achievements following World War I. <u>Abstract</u> art became even more popular. There was a fascination with the absurd and the unconscious. The idea that the world did not make sense gave rise to two movements, Dadaism and surrealism. Dadaists were artists who were obsessed with the idea that life has no purpose. They tried to express the insanity of life in their art. Dada artist Hannah Höch, for example, used **photomontage** (a picture made of a combination of photographs) to comment on women's roles in the new mass culture. Another movement, **surrealism,** sought a reality beyond the material world and found it in the world of the unconscious. Surrealists portrayed fantasies, dreams, and even nightmares to show this greater reality. Salvador Dalí was one of the foremost surrealists. He painted everyday objects but separated them from their normal contexts. By placing recognizable objects in unrecognizable relationships, Dalí created a strange world in which the irrational became visible.

In the 1920s, Weimar Germany was one of the chief European centers for modern arts and sciences. Hitler and the Nazis, however, rejected modern art as "degenerate." They believed that they could create a new and genuine German art. It would glorify the strong, the healthy, and the heroic. The new German art was actually derived from nineteenth-century folk art and emphasized realistic scenes of everyday life.

The field of architecture also changed after World War I. Walter Gropius formed the Bauhaus school for architects in Weimar, Germany in 1919, where architects would be trained to create a "new structure of the future." Hitler shut down this modernist school because he was opposed to the rational, functional designs and favored buildings that glorified the Nazi cause.

The interest in the unconscious was also found in new literary techniques. "Stream of consciousness" was a technique used by writers to show the thoughts of each character. The most famous example of this technique is the novel *Ulysses* by James Joyce. The German writer Hermann Hesse dealt with the unconscious in a different way. His novels reflect the influence of both Freud's psychology and Asian religions. In *Siddhartha* and *Steppenwolf,* Hesse used Buddhist ideas to show the psychological confusion of modern existence.

6. What did Hitler and the Nazis think about modern art?

_____

_____

Academic Vocabulary
incapable: lacking capacity or ability to accomplish a goal (p. 488)

Academic Vocabulary
abstract: having only intrinsic form with little or no attempt at pictorial representation or narrative content (p. 488)

Reading Essentials and Study Guide

Chapter 9, Section 4 *(continued)*

- ## The Heroic Age of Physics *(page 491)*

The revolution in physics begun by Albert Einstein continued after World War I. One physicist, Ernest Rutherford, called the 1920s the "heroic age of physics." The <u>classical</u> physics of Newton had made people believe that all phenomena could be defined and predicted. In 1927, this belief was shaken when the German physicist Werner Heisenberg explained an observation that he called the **uncertainty principle.** This theory suggests that all physical laws that govern the universe are based in uncertainty. The foundation for the uncertainty principle is the fact that the behavior of subatomic particles is unpredictable. The theory's emphasis on randomness and uncertainty challenged Newtonian physics and represented a new worldview.

Academic Vocabulary
classical: not involving relativity, wave mechanics, or quantum theory (p. 491)

7. What scientific fact was the foundation for the uncertainty principle?

_____

_____

_____

_____

_____

Reading Essentials and Study Guide

Chapter 10, Section 1

For use with textbook pages 501–506

NATIONALISM IN THE MIDDLE EAST

CONTENT VOCABULARY

genocide the deliberate mass murder of a particular racial, political, or cultural group *(page 503)*

ethnic cleansing a policy of killing or forcibly removing an ethnic group from its lands, used during the Bosnian War of 1993 to 1996 *(page 503)*

DRAWING FROM EXPERIENCE

What do you think of when you hear the words "genocide" and "ethnic cleansing"? Has genocide been practiced anywhere during your lifetime? In what parts of the world?

In this section, you will learn how the decline and fall of the Ottoman Empire led to the creation of the Turkish Republic. You will also learn how Persia became the modern state of Iran and how changes in the Middle East after World War I led to conflicts in that region that continue today.

> **California History Social Science Standards**
>
> **10.5** Students analyze the causes and course of the First World War.
> **10.6** Students analyze the effects of the First World War.
>
> **Focuses on:**
> 10.5.5, 10.6.2

ORGANIZING YOUR THOUGHTS

Use the diagram below to help you take notes. Trace the loss of territories that gradually reduced the Ottoman Empire to the area of present-day Turkey.

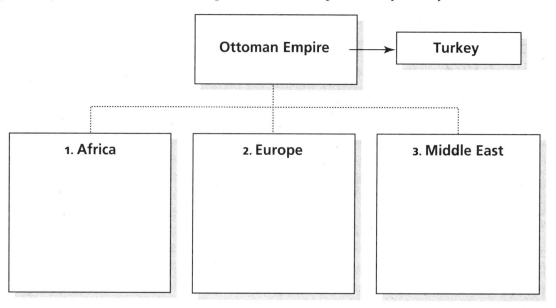

Reading Essentials and Study Guide

Chapter 10, Section 1 *(continued)*

READ TO LEARN

- **Decline and Fall of the Ottoman Empire** *(page 502)*

The Ottoman Empire had been growing weaker since the end of the eighteenth century. Its size had decreased dramatically. In North Africa, Ottoman rule had ended in the nineteenth century when France seized Algeria and Tunisia and Great Britain took control of Egypt. Greece also declared its independence in the nineteenth century.

In 1876, reformers took control of the empire's government. They adopted a constitution with the goal of forming a legislative assembly. But the sultan they put on the throne, Abdulhamid II, suspended the new constitution. The constitution then became a symbol of change to a group of reformers named the Young Turks. This group forced the restoration of the constitution in 1908. They deposed the sultan in 1909.

The Ottoman Empire came to an end after World War I. The Ottoman government allied with Germany. As a result, the British tried to undermine the Ottoman Empire by supporting Arab nationalists in the Arabian Peninsula. In 1916, the local governor of Makkah declared Arabia's independence. British troops seized Palestine.

During the war, the Ottoman Turks practiced **genocide**—the deliberate mass murder of a particular racial, political, or cultural group. (A similar practice would be called **ethnic cleansing** in the Bosnian War in the 1990s.) The Christian Armenians were a minority in the Ottoman Empire. They had been demanding their independence for years. In 1915, the government reacted to an Armenian uprising by killing Armenian men and deporting (sending out of the country) women and children. By 1918, 1.4 million Armenians had been killed.

At the end of World War I, the Ottoman Empire collapsed. Great Britain and France divided up territories in the Middle East. Greece invaded Turkey and seized western parts of the Anatolian Peninsula. As a result of this invasion, Colonel Mustafa Kemal called for the creation of an elected government. His forces drove the Greeks from the Anatolian Peninsula. The Ottoman sultans fled the country, which was now declared to be the Turkish Republic. Colonel Kemal became president.

4. Why did the British support Arab nationalists during World War I?

_____

_____

_____

_____

Reading Essentials and Study Guide

Chapter 10, Section 1 (continued)

• The Modernization of Turkey (page 504)

President Kemal was now known as Atatürk ("father Turk"). A democratic system was put in place. But Kemal did not allow opposition and suppressed his critics. He tried to transform Turkey into a modern state. Many Arabic elements were eliminated from the Turkish language. Popular education was introduced. All Turkish citizens were forced to adopt family (last names), like Europeans. Factories were established, and a five-year plan was developed for the economy.

Academic Vocabulary
eliminate: to cast out or get rid of (p. 504)

Academic Vocabulary
establish: to introduce (p. 504)

Atatürk also tried to break the power of the Islamic religion. He wanted to make Turkey a secular state (a state that does not favor particular religions). The caliphate was abolished in 1924. Men were forbidden to wear the fez, the cap worn by Turkish Muslims. Women were forbidden to wear the veil, an Islamic custom. New laws gave women marriage and inheritance rights. In 1934, women received the right to vote. All citizens were given the right to convert to other religions.

5. In what ways did Atatürk try to break the power of Islam in Turkey?

_____

_____

_____

_____

• The Beginnings of Modern Iran (page 505)

In Persia, the Qajar dynasty (1794–1925) had not been very successful in resolving the country's problems. The discovery of oil in the country in 1908 attracted foreign interest. The presence of more and more foreigners led to the rise of a Persian nationalist movement. In 1921, Reza Khan led a military uprising that took control of Tehran, the capital. In 1925, Reza Khan made himself the shah (king) and was called Reza Shah Pahlavi. He introduced a number of reforms to modernize the government, the military, and the economic system. He did not try to destroy Islamic beliefs, but he did encourage a Western-style educational system. He also forbade women to wear the veil in public.

Persia became the modern state of Iran in 1935. To free himself from Great Britain and the Soviet Union, Reza Shah Pahlavi drew closer to Nazi Germany. The Soviet Union and Great Britain sent troops to Iran during World War II. Reza Shah Pahlavi resigned in protest and was replaced by his son, Mohammad Reza Pahlavi.

Reading Essentials and Study Guide

Chapter 10, Section 1 *(continued)*

6. What were some of the changes that Reza Shah Pahlavi made in Persia?

_____

_____

_____

_____

_____

• **Arab Nationalism** *(page 505)*

World War I gave Arabs the chance to escape from Ottoman rule. The Arabs were not an actual nation, but a collection of peoples united by language and religion. Great Britain had supported Arab nationalists in 1916. The nationalists hoped that this support would continue after the war. Instead, France and Britain created mandates in the area. These mandates were territories that had previously been part of the Ottoman Empire but were now supervised by the League of Nations. Great Britain was given the right to govern Iraq and Jordan. France governed Syria and Lebanon. In most of these nations, the Europeans determined the borders and divided the peoples. In most cases, the people in each newly-defined country did not identify strongly with that country. But they continued to have a sense of Arab nationalism.

In the early 1920s, a reform leader, Ibn Saud, united Arabs in the northern part of the Arabian Peninsula. Ibn Saud had a great deal of support among Arab peoples. He created the kingdom of Saudi Arabia in 1932. (The word Saudi comes from his name.) At first, Saudi Arabia was very poor. Muslim pilgrimages to Makkah and Madinah were its main source of income. During the 1930s, however, U.S. prospectors began to explore for oil. Standard Oil found oil at Dhahran on the Persian Gulf in 1938. As a result of these oil explorations, Saudi Arabia became a base for many Western oil industries that brought the promise of wealth.

7. Who determined the borders of most of the nations in the Middle East following World War I?

_____

_____

_____

_____

_____

Reading Essentials and Study Guide

Chapter 10, Section 1 *(continued)*

• The Problem of Palestine *(page 506)*

The situation in Palestine made problems in the Middle East more complicated. Both Jews and Muslim Arabs felt they had a claim to the region as their homeland. Jews had lived there in ancient times but in the first century A.D. they were forced into exile. As a result, Muslim Arabs made up the majority of the population, although many Jews continued to live there. In the 1890s, a Zionist movement argued that Palestine should be established as a Jewish state. Then during World War I, the British issued the Balfour Declaration. It supported the idea that Palestine should be a national home for the Jews, but it also said that the rights of the non-Jewish population should be protected.

The Balfour Declaration drew many Jews to Palestine. In the 1930s, many Jews also fled to Palestine because of Nazi persecution and violence against them. Muslim Arabs began to protest the growing number of Jews, and there were several outbreaks of violence. In 1939, the British responded by allowing only 75,000 Jewish immigrants into Palestine over the next five years. After that, no more Jews could enter the country. This policy intensified the tension and violence.

8. What was the Balfour Declaration? What were some of its results?

_____

_____

_____

_____

Reading Essentials and Study Guide

Chapter 10, Section 2

For use with textbook pages 507–513

NATIONALISM IN AFRICA AND ASIA

CONTENT VOCABULARY

Pan-Africanism a movement that stressed the need for the unity of all Africans *(page 509)*

Mahatma ("Great Soul") the name given to Mohandas Gandhi by the Indian people *(page 510)*

civil disobedience refusal to obey laws considered to be unjust *(page 510)*

zaibatsu a large financial and industrial corporation in Japan *(page 511)*

California History Social Science Standards

10.3 Students analyze the effects of the Industrial Revolution in England, France, Germany, Japan, and the United States.

10.4 Students analyze patterns of global change in the era of New Imperialism in at least two of the following regions or countries: Africa, Southeast Asia, China, India, Latin America and the Philippines.

10.5 Students analyze the causes and course of the First World War.

10.7 Students analyze the rise of totalitarian governments after the First World War.

10.8 Students analyze the causes and consequences of World War II.

Focuses on:
10.3.5, 10.4.1, 10.4.2, 10.4.4, 10.5.4, 10.8.1

DRAWING FROM EXPERIENCE

Have you ever thought that a rule was unfair? How could you protest this rule in a nonviolent way?

In the last section, you read about the end of the Ottoman Empire and the rise of nationalism in the Middle East. In this section, you will read about nationalism in Africa and Asia. In India, the followers of Mahatma Gandhi used the methods of civil disobedience to protest British laws.

ORGANIZING YOUR THOUGHTS

Use the chart below to help you take notes. Leaders of reform and independence movements in parts of Africa and Asia used various methods to protest colonial rule. Identify the countries of the following leaders and summarize the methods that they used.

Leader	Country	Methods of Protest
Harry Thuku	1.	2.
Omar Mukhtar	3.	4.
Nnamdi Azikiwe	5.	6.
Mohandas Gandhi	7.	8.
Ho Chi Minh	9.	10.

Reading Essentials and Study Guide

Chapter 10, Section 2 (continued)

READ TO LEARN

- ## Movements Toward Independence in Africa *(page 508)*

Black Africans fought in World War I in British and French armies. Many Africans hoped that they would be rewarded with independence after the war. But the peace settlement after World War I was a big disappointment. Germany lost its African colonies, but they were given to Great Britain and France as mandates. Britain and France now controlled much of Africa.

After World War I, Africans became more active in politics. The Africans who had fought in the war became <u>aware</u> of new ideas about freedom and nationalism. Many Africans decided to seek reforms. In Kenya, Harry Thuku organized the Young Kikuyu Association. In 1921, it protested the high taxes imposed by the British. Thuku was arrested. When an angry crowd demanded his release, government forces fired on the crowd and killed at least 20 people. In Libya, forces led by Omar Mukhtar used guerrilla warfare against the Italians and defeated them several times. The Italians reacted by creating concentration camps and using modern weapons against the revolt. Mukhtar's death ended the revolt. Although the colonial powers often used force against independence movements, they also began to make reforms. But the reforms were too few and too late. By the 1930s, more and more African leaders were calling for independence, not reform.

Academic Vocabulary
aware: having or showing realization, perception, or knowledge (p. 508)

Many of the new African leaders had been educated in Europe and the United States. They were influenced by the ideas of W.E.B. Du Bois and Marcus Garvey. Du Bois was an African American educated at Harvard University. He was the leader of a movement for full civil and political equality. Garvey was a Jamaican who lived in Harlem. He stressed the need for the unity of all Africans, a movement known as **Pan-Africanism.** His *Declaration of the Rights of the Negro Peoples of the World* had a strong impact on African leaders. Jomo Kenyatta of Kenya wrote a book, *Facing Mount Kenya,* in which he argued that British rule was destroying the traditional culture of African peoples. Léopold Senghor, a poet, organized an independence movement in Senegal. Nnamdi Azikiwe of Nigeria began a newspaper, *The West African Pilot*. He believed in nonviolence as a method to gain independence. Despite the efforts of these leaders, the independence movements in Africa were not successful until after World War II.

11. How did an African American and a Jamaican in the United States influence many of the new African leaders in the 1920s and 1930s?

_____

_____

_____

_____

Reading Essentials and Study Guide

Chapter 10, Section 2 (continued)

• The Movement for Indian Independence (page 510)

Mohandas Gandhi had become active in the movement for Indian self-rule before World War I. The Indian people began to call him India's "Great Soul," or **Mahatma.** He began to organize mass protests to achieve his goals. He believed in nonviolence and protested British laws by using the methods of **civil disobedience** (refusal to obey laws considered to be unjust). In 1919, the protests led to violence. In response, British troops killed hundreds of protesters. Gandhi was arrested for his role in protests against British rule and spent several years in prison.

In 1935, Great Britain passed the Government of India Act. It gave Indians a greater role in the governing process. The Legislative Council became a two-house parliament. Two-thirds of its members were to be elected. Five million Indians were given the right to vote, although this was still only a small percentage of the total population.

The Indian National Congress (INC) had been founded in 1885 to try to reform Britain's government of India. Reforms were no longer enough for many of the members of the INC. Motilal Nehru, the new leader of the INC, pushed for full independence.

Gandhi was released from prison and returned to his policy of civil disobedience. Nonviolence was still at the center of his policy. Gandhi led a protest against the British salt tax. Britain had increased the tax and prohibited the Indian people from manufacturing or harvesting their own salt. In 1930, Gandhi and his supporters walked to the sea. This became known as the Salt March. When they reached the coast, Gandhi picked up a pinch of salt. Thousands of Indians did the same thing. Gandhi and many other members of the INC were arrested.

In the 1930s, there was a new leader in the Indian independence movement. Jawaharlal Nehru was a new kind of Indian politician. He was upper-class and intellectual. He had studied law in Great Britain. The independence movement now split into two paths. Gandhi's movement was religious and traditional. Nehru's movement was secular and modern. Hostility between Muslims and Hindus complicated the situation in India even further. Muslims were dissatisfied with the INC because Hindus dominated it. By the 1930s, the Muslim League was starting to believe in the creation of a separate Muslim state of Pakistan in the northwest part of the country.

12. In what ways were Gandhi's and Nehru's independence movements different?

_____

_____

_____

Reading Essentials and Study Guide

Chapter 10, Section 2 (continued)

• The Rise of a Militarist Japan (page 511)

The economic and social reforms of the Meiji Era had made Japan prosperous. A modern industrial and commercial sector had developed. The political system also became more Western. In the Japanese economy, various manufacturing processes were concentrated within large financial and industrial corporations called *zaibatsu*. The *zaibatsu* often received government help and developed into vast companies that controlled major segments of the Japanese economy. The concentration of wealth led to economic inequalities. City workers were poorly paid and had poor housing. A rapid increase in population led to food shortages. Inflation in food prices led to food riots. When the Great Depression struck, workers and farmers suffered the most. Many Japanese people began to call for a return to traditional values. They also demanded that Japan use its strength to dominate Asia.

In the early twentieth century, Japan began to have difficulty finding sources of raw materials and foreign markets for its manufactured goods. Japan had dealt with the problem by seizing territories, such as Formosa, Korea, and southern Manchuria. The United States was concerned about Japanese expansion. In 1922, the U.S. held a conference of nations that had interests in the Pacific. The conference produced a treaty that maintained the Open Door policy in China and recognized the territorial <u>integrity</u> of China. Japan accepted the treaty in return for recognition of its control of southern Manchuria. However, as the Japanese expanded into new industries, the Japanese government came under increasing pressure to find new sources of raw materials.

Academic Vocabulary
integrity: the quality or state of being complete and undivided (p. 512)

During the first part of the twentieth century, Japan moved toward a more democratic government. The parliament and political parties grew stronger. However, at the end of the 1920s, new problems caused militant forces to become more powerful. Some of the militants were civilians who were convinced that the government had been corrupted by Western ideas. Others were members of the military who were angered by cuts in military spending and the government's pacifist policies. In the 1930s, civilians and members of the army and navy formed extremist patriotic organizations. One group of army officers invaded Manchuria in 1931, without government permission. Within a short time, all of Manchuria was conquered.

The Japanese government opposed the conquest of Manchuria, but the Japanese people supported it. The military and other supporters of Japanese expansion soon dominated the government. Japan was put on wartime status. A military draft was started in 1938. The economy came under government control. Labor unions were disbanded. Education and culture were purged of most Western ideas. Militant leaders stressed traditional Japanese values.

Reading Essentials and Study Guide

Chapter 10, Section 2 *(continued)*

13. How did industrialization in Japan lead to the rise of militarism?

_____

_____

_____

_____

_____

• Nationalism and Revolution in Asia *(page 513)*

Before World War I, Marxism had no appeal for most Asians. Most Asian societies were agricultural and did not seem ready for revolution. After the revolution in Russia, the situation began to change. The Russian Revolution showed that a Marxist revolution could work even in a country that was not fully industrialized. In 1919, the Communist International, or Comintern, was formed. It was a worldwide organization of Communist parties that worked for world revolution. At its headquarters in Moscow, agents were trained and then returned to their own countries to form Marxist parties and promote revolution. By the end of the 1920s, nearly every colonial society in Asia had a Communist party.

In some countries, the Communists were able to work with nationalists to fight Western imperialism. This was true in French Indochina, where Vietnamese Communists were organized by Ho Chi Minh, who had been trained in Moscow. A strong Communist-nationalist alliance was also formed in China. In most colonial societies, however, Communist parties had little success in the 1930s.

14. What was the Comintern?

_____

_____

_____

_____

_____

Reading Essentials and Study Guide

Chapter 10, Section 3

For use with textbook pages 514–519

REVOLUTIONARY CHAOS IN CHINA

CONTENT VOCABULARY

guerrilla tactics military maneuvers, such as sabotage and subterfuge, based on the element of surprise *(page 516)*

redistribution of wealth shifting of wealth from a rich minority to a poor majority *(page 519)*

DRAWING FROM EXPERIENCE

What do you know about China? What kind of government does it have? What is life like for the people living there? What is the main way of making a living in China?

In the last two sections, you read about nationalism in Africa, Asia, and the Middle East. In this section, you will read about the conflict between Nationalists and Communists for control of China.

ORGANIZING YOUR THOUGHTS

Use the chart below to help you take notes. Chiang Kai-shek established a Nationalist government over China in 1928. Summarize the programs and projects of Chiang Kai-shek as they relate to the areas in this chart.

California History Social Science Standards

10.4 Students analyze patterns of global change in the era of New Imperialism in at least two of the following regions or countries: Africa, Southeast Asia, China, India, Latin America and the Philippines.
10.9 Students analyze the international developments in the post-World War II world.

Focuses on:
10.4.4, 10.9.4

Programs and Projects of Chiang Kai-shek	
Values	1.
Transportation	2.
Economy	3.
Education	4.
Government	5.

Reading Essentials and Study Guide

Chapter 10, Section 3 *(continued)*

READ TO LEARN

•Nationalists and Communists *(page 515)*

In 1921, a group of young radicals founded the Chinese Communist Party (CCP) in Shanghai. Comintern agents advised the new party to join with the more experienced Nationalist Party. Sun Yat-sen, the leader of the Nationalist Party, welcomed the cooperation. In 1923, the two parties formed an alliance to oppose the warlords and drive the imperialist powers out of China. For three years, the two parties worked together. They trained a revolutionary army to march north and seize control of China. This Northern Expedition began in the summer of 1926. By the following spring, these forces had taken control of all China south of the Chang Jiang (Yangtze River).

Tensions between the two parties eventually caused problems. Sun Yat-sen died in 1925 and was succeeded by Chiang Kai-shek as head of the Nationalist Party. Chiang pretended to support the alliance with the Communists. But in April 1927, he attacked the Communists in Shanghai. Thousands were killed in what is called the Shanghai Massacre. The Communist-Nationalist alliance came to an end. In 1928, Chiang Kai-shek founded a new Chinese republic at Nanjing. During the next three years, he worked to reunify China.

6. What two parties formed an alliance in 1923 to drive the imperialist powers out of China?

_____

_____

_____

• The Communists in Hiding *(page 516)*

After the Shanghai Massacre, most of the Communist leaders went into hiding in Shanghai. Some party members fled to Jiangxi Province. The young Communist organizer Mao Zedong led them. Mao was convinced that peasants in the countryside instead of the urban working class would lead a Chinese revolution.

Chiang Kai-shek tried to force the Communists out of hiding in Shanghai. In 1931, most Communist party leaders were forced to flee to Mao's base in South China. Chiang then turned his forces against Mao's base. Chiang's forces far outnumbered Mao's, but Mao made effective use of **guerrilla tactics** (using unexpected maneuvers like sabotage and sub-terfuge to fight the enemy) to <u>pursue</u> the enemy.

Academic Vocabulary
pursue: to follow in order to overtake, capture, kill, or defeat (p. 516)

Reading Essentials and Study Guide

Chapter 10, Section 3 *(continued)*

7. How did Mao Zedong believe that a Chinese revolution would take place?

_____

_____

_____

_____

● **The Long March** *(page 517)*

In 1934, Chiang's troops surrounded the Communist base in Jiangxi. But Mao's army, the People's Liberation Army (PLA), broke through the Nationalist lines and began its famous Long March. Mao's army traveled almost 6,000 miles on foot through mountains, marshes, and deserts. One year later, they reached safety in North China. Only nine thousand of the original ninety thousand survived the journey. In the course of the Long March, Mao Zedong had become the sole leader of the Chinese Communist Party.

8. What was the Long March?

_____

_____

_____

_____

● **The New China of Chiang Kai-shek** *(page 518)*

In the meantime, Chiang Kai-shek had been trying to build a new nation. He was committed to the plans of Sun Yat-sen, which called for a republican government. First, there would be a transitional period. Chiang announced a period of political training to prepare people for constitutional government. The Nationalists also tried to carry out a land-reform program and to modernize industry.

Creating a new China was not easy, however. Most rural people were drained by civilstrife. The peasants were still very poor, and most of them were illiterate. Chiang Kai-shek was aware of the problem of introducing foreign ideas into a conservative population. He tried to combine modern Western innovations with traditional Confucian values of hard work, obedience, and integrity. He set up a "New Life Movement" and promoted traditional Confucian ethics. It also rejected the individualism and material greed that was associated with Western capitalism.

Academic Vocabulary
constitutional: loyal to or supporting an established constitution or form of government (p. 518)

Reading Essentials and Study Guide

Chapter 10, Section 3 *(continued)*

Chiang Kai-shek had other problems. His government only had total control over a few provinces in the Chang Jiang Valley. The Japanese threatened to gain control of northern China. The Great Depression was also having a negative effect on China's economy. But Chiang did have some success. He undertook a huge road-building program and added to the country's railroad system. He also set up a national bank and improved the educational system. But he was less successful in other areas. His land-reform program had little effect. Because wealthy landowners and the urban middle class supported him, he did not push for programs that would lead to a **redistribution of wealth** (the shifting of wealth from a rich minority to a poor majority). His government was also repressive. Chiang was afraid of Communist influence and suppressed all opposition. By doing so, he alienated many intellectuals and political moderates.

9. What was the New Life Movement? What were some of its goals?

_____

_____

_____

_____

_____

Reading Essentials and Study Guide

Chapter 10, Section 4

For use with textbook pages 520–525

NATIONALISM IN LATIN AMERICA

CONTENT VOCABULARY
oligarchy a government where a select group of people exercises control *(page 522)*

DRAWING FROM EXPERIENCE

What goods do you use that are imported from Mexico or another Latin American country? Do you eat food grown in these countries? Do you wear clothes made in one of these countries?

In the last three sections, you read about nationalism in Africa, Asia, and the Middle East. In this section, you will read about nationalism and the rise of dictatorships in Latin America during the early twentieth century. The Latin American economy at this time was based largely on the export of food and raw materials to the United States and other countries.

ORGANIZING YOUR THOUGHTS

Use the diagram below to help you take notes. Instability caused by the Great Depression led to the creation of many military dictatorships in Latin America in the 1930s. Describe the governments in Argentina, Brazil, and Mexico during the 1930s.

> **California History Social Science Standards**
>
> **10.3** Students analyze the effects of the Industrial Revolution in England, France, Germany, Japan, and the United States.
> **10.4** Students analyze patterns of global change in the era of New Imperialism in at least two of the following regions or countries: Africa, Southeast Asia, China, India, Latin America and the Philippines.
> **10.6** Students analyze the effects of the First World War.
> **10.9** Students analyze the international developments in the post-World War II world.
> **Focuses on:**
> 10.3.5, 10.4.1, 10.6.4, 10.9

Country	Government in the 1930s
Argentina	1.
Brazil	2.
Mexico	3.

Reading Essentials and Study Guide

Chapter 10, Section 4 *(continued)*

• The Latin American Economy *(page 521)*

At the beginning of the twentieth century, the Latin American economy was based on the export of food and raw materials. The economies of some countries depended on the export of only one or two products. Argentina exported beef and wheat; Chile, nitrates and copper; Brazil and Caribbean nations, sugar; and Central America, bananas. Although a few people made big profits, most people gained little from these exports.

Beginning in the 1920s, the United States began to replace Great Britain as the biggest investor in Latin America. U.S. investors put their funds directly into production companies and ran the companies themselves. As a result, large segments of Latin America's export industries came into U.S. hands.

Latin Americans were angry that U.S. investors controlled so many Latin American industries. Many Latin Americans viewed the United States as an imperialist power. They pointed out that profits from U.S. businesses were sometimes used to keep ruthless dictators in power. The United States had intervened militarily in Latin America for years. This was especially true in Central America and the Caribbean. In 1933, however, President Franklin Roosevelt announced the Good Neighbor policy. This policy rejected the use of U.S. military force in Latin America. Roosevelt withdrew the last U.S. marines from Haiti in 1934.

The Great Depression was a disaster for Latin America's economy. There was a decreased demand for Latin American products and raw materials, especially coffee, sugar, metals, and wheat. The countries that depended on the export of only one product were especially damaged. There was one positive effect, however. With a decline in exports, Latin American countries no longer had the money to buy imported goods. Many Latin American governments encouraged the development of new industries to produce goods that had previously been imported. Governments often invested in the new industries. This led to government-run industries in Chile, Brazil, Argentina, and Mexico.

4. What were the effects of the Great Depression on Latin America's economy?

_____

_____

_____

_____

_____

_____

Reading Essentials and Study Guide

Chapter 10, Section 4 *(continued)*

• The Move to Authoritarianism *(page 522)*

Most Latin American countries had republican forms of government. In reality, however, a small group of church officials, military leaders, and large landowners dominated each country. They were kept in power by military forces. Military leaders often took control of the government. This trend toward authoritarianism increased during the 1930s, mainly because of the impact of the Great Depression. The trend was especially evident in Argentina, Brazil, and Mexico.

Argentina was controlled by an **oligarchy** (a government where a select group of people exercises control). This oligarchy of large landowners had grown wealthy from the export of beef and wheat. It did not realize the growing importance of industry and cities. It also ignored the growing middle class. The middle class reacted by forming the Radical Party in 1890. In 1916, Hipólito Irigoyen, leader of the Radical Party, was elected president of Argentina. The Radical Party was afraid of the industrial workers, who used strikes to improve working conditions. As a result, it drew closer to the large landowners and became more corrupt. The military was also concerned about the power of the industrial workers. In 1930, the Argentine army overthrew President Irigoyen and put the large landowners back in power in an attempt to <u>stimulate</u> the old export economy. During World War II, military officers formed a new organization, known as the Group of United Officers (GOU). They were unhappy with the government and overthrew it in June 1943. Three years later, Juan Perón, a GOU member, was elected president of Argentina.

> **Academic Vocabulary**
>
> **stimulate:** to motivate activity or growth (p. 523)

In Brazil, the army had overthrown the monarchy in 1889 and established a republic. The republic was controlled mainly by the large landowners, who had become wealthy by growing coffee. The Great Depression devastated the coffee industry, and the landowners were no longer able to <u>maintain</u> their power. In 1930, a military coup made Getúlio Vargas, a wealthy rancher, president of Brazil. He ruled from 1930 to 1945. He tried to win the support of workers by establishing an eight-hour workday and a minimum wage. In 1937, Vargas made himself dictator. Beginning in 1938, he established his New State. It was an authoritarian state with some fascist-like features. Political parties were outlawed and civil rights restricted. A secret police used torture against Vargas's enemies. Vargas also encouraged new industries. The government established the Brazilian steel industry and set up a company to explore for oil.

> **Academic Vocabulary**
>
> **maintain:** to sustain against opposition or danger; uphold and defend (p. 523)

Mexico was not an authoritarian state, but it was not truly democratic. The official political party of the Mexican Revolution, known as the Institutional Revolutionary Party (PRI), controlled the major groups in Mexican society. Party bosses of the PRI chose the party's presidential candidate, who was then elected by the people. Change began when Lázaro Cárdenas became president in 1934. He distributed 44 million acres of land to Mexican peasants. He also

Reading Essentials and Study Guide

Chapter 10, Section 4 *(continued)*

took a strong stand with the United States, especially over oil. After a dispute over workers' wages, the Cárdenas government seized control of the oil fields and the property of the oil companies. The U.S. oil companies were furious and asked President Roosevelt to intervene. He refused, because of the Good Neighbor policy. Eventually, the Mexican government paid the oil companies for their property. It then set up PEMEX, a national oil company.

5. What were some of the changes that Cárdenas made after he became president of Mexico?

_____

_____

_____

_____

_____

• Culture in Latin America *(page 524)*

During the early twentieth century, European artistic and literary movements began to have an impact on Latin America. In major cities, the wealthy were interested in the work of modern artists. Latin American artists went abroad and brought back modern techniques. Many artists and writers used their work to promote a new national spirit. The Mexican artist Diego Rivera is one example. He used murals. His works were aimed at the masses of people, many of whom could not read. He tried to create a national art that would show Mexico's past and its festivals and folk customs. His work also had a political and social message. Rivera did not want people to forget the Mexican Revolution, which had overthrown large landowners and foreign interests.

6. What were some of the goals that Diego Rivera tried to achieve with his art?

_____

_____

_____

_____

_____

Reading Essentials and Study Guide

Chapter 11, Section 1

For use with textbook pages 535–540

PATHS TO WAR

CONTENT VOCABULARY

demilitarized an area that is free of weapons or fortifications *(page 536)*

appeasement a policy of satisfying the demands of a dissatisfied power in an effort to maintain peace and stability *(page 537)*

New Order a new Asian order including Japan, China, and Manchuria, that would result in Asian prosperity *(page 539)*

sanction a restriction intended to enforce international law *(page 540)*

DRAWING FROM EXPERIENCE

How do you resolve conflicts with other people? Do you ever give in to their demands in order to avoid conflict?

In this section, you will learn about the actions of Germany and Japan that paved the way for the start of World War II. In an attempt to avoid war, some European countries initially gave in to Hitler's demands to occupy other territories.

> **California History Social Science Standards**
>
> **10.7** Students analyze the rise of totalitarian governments after the First World War.
> **10.8** Students analyze the causes and consequences of World War II.
>
> **Focuses on:**
> 10.7.3, 10.8.1, 10.8.2

ORGANIZING YOUR THOUGHTS

Use the time line below to help you take notes. From 1936 to 1939, Hitler became more and more aggressive and invaded more and more territories. Trace Hitler's acts of aggression during these years.

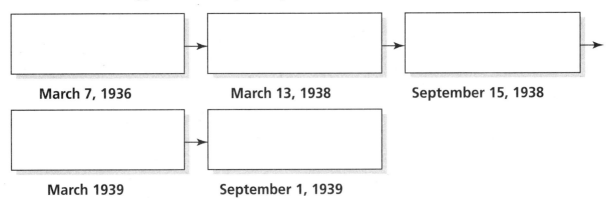

March 7, 1936 → March 13, 1938 → September 15, 1938 →

March 1939 → September 1, 1939

Reading Essentials and Study Guide

Chapter 11, Section 1 *(continued)*

READ TO LEARN

• The German Path to War *(page 536)*

World War II had its roots in the beliefs of Adolf Hitler. He believed that Germans belonged to a so-called Aryan race that was superior to all other races and nationalities. He also believed that Germany was capable of building a great civilization and needed more land in order to become a great power. Hitler planned to conquer the Soviet Union and use the Slavic peoples for slave <u>labor</u>.

After World War I, the Treaty of Versailles had limited Germany's military power. At first, Hitler said that Germany wanted to revise the unfair provisions of the treaty by peaceful means. However, on March 9, 1935, Hitler announced the creation of a new air force. One week later, he began a military draft. Hitler was convinced that the Western states had no intention of using force to maintain the Treaty of Versailles. On March 7, 1936, he sent German troops into the Rhineland. The Rhineland was part of Germany, but it was a **demilitarized** area. According to the Treaty of Versailles, Germany was not permitted to have weapons or fortifications there. France had the right to use force against any violation of the demilitarized area but would not act without British support. Great Britain did not support the use of force against Germany. Great Britain began to practice a policy of **appeasement.** This policy was based on the belief that if European states satisfied the reasonable demands of dissatisfied powers, the dissatisfied powers would be content, and peace would be <u>achieved</u>.

Meanwhile, Hitler gained new allies. Fascist Italy invaded Ethiopia in October 1935. France and Britain were opposed to this invasion. This made Mussolini angry, and he welcomed Hitler's support. In 1936, Mussolini and Hitler made an agreement that recognized their common political and economic interests. This new alliance was known as the Rome-Berlin Axis. Germany and Japan signed the Anti-Comintern Pact, in which they promised to maintain a common front against communism.

By 1937, Hitler decided to pursue one of his goals: union with Austria, his native land. He threatened Austria with invasion. This forced the Austrian chancellor to put Austrian Nazis in charge of the government. The new government invited German troops to enter Austria. On March 13, 1938, Hitler annexed Austria to Germany.

Hitler's next goal was the destruction of Czechoslovakia. On September 15, 1938, he demanded that Germany be given the Sudetenland, an area in northwestern Czechoslovakia. Most of the people who lived in this area were Germans. Hitler said that he was willing to risk "world war" to achieve his objective. At a <u>conference</u> in Munich, Britain, France, Germany, and Italy reached an agreement that gave Hitler nearly all of his demands. German troops were allowed to occupy the Sudetenland. The Czechs stood by helplessly. Neville Chamberlain, the British prime minister, boasted that the

Academic Vocabulary
labor: human activity that provides the goods or services in the economy (p. 536)

Academic Vocabulary
achieve: to reach a goal; accomplish (p. 537)

Academic Vocabulary
conference: a meeting of two or more people to discuss common problems and concerns (p. 537)

Reading Essentials and Study Guide

Chapter 11, Section 1 (continued)

agreement meant "peace for our time." Hitler had promised Chamberlain that he would make no more demands. Like many others, Chamberlain believed Hitler's promises. In fact, Hitler was more convinced than ever that the Western democracies were weak and would not fight. In March 1939, Hitler invaded and took control of Bohemia and Moravia in western Czechoslovakia.

At last, the Western nations reacted to the Nazi threat. Hitler's aggression had made clear that his promises were worthless. When Hitler began to demand the Polish port of Danzig, Great Britain offered to protect Poland in the event of war. At the same time, both France and Britain realized that they needed the Soviet Union in order to stop Nazi aggression. They began negotiations with Joseph Stalin, the Soviet dictator. Hitler was afraid that the West and the Soviet Union might make an alliance. To keep this from happening, Hitler made his own agreement with Joseph Stalin. On August 23, 1939, Germany and the Soviet Union signed the Nazi-Soviet Nonaggression Pact. In it, the two nations promised not to attack each other. To get Stalin to sign the pact, Hitler offered Stalin control of eastern Poland and the Baltic states. On September 1, 1939, German forces invaded Poland. Two days later, Britain and France declared war on Germany.

6. Why did Great Britain give in to so many of Hitler's demands?

_____

_____

_____

_____

_____

• The Japanese Path to War (page 539)

By the mid-1930s, militants had gained control of Japanese politics. In September 1931, Japanese soldiers had seized Manchuria, because Manchuria had natural resources that Japan needed. As an excuse for seizing Manchuria, Japan pointed to a Chinese attack on a Japanese railway near the city of Mukden. In fact, Japanese soldiers disguised as Chinese had carried out the "Mukden incident." Worldwide protests led the League of Nations to send investigators to Manchuria. When the investigators issued a report condemning the seizure, Japan withdrew from the League. Over the next several years, Japan strengthened its hold on Manchuria. Japan now began to expand into North China.

Because of the threat from Communists within China, Chiang Kai-shek tried to avoid conflict with Japan. He tried to appease Japan by allowing it to govern areas in North China. When Japan began to move southward, Chiang

Reading Essentials and Study Guide

Chapter 11, Section 1 *(continued)*

was forced to end his military efforts against the Communists. In 1936, he formed a new united front against the Japanese. In July 1937, Chinese and Japanese forces clashed south of Beijing. This incident turned into a major conflict. The Japanese seized the Chinese capital of Nanjing. Chiang Kai-shek refused to surrender and moved his government upriver.

Japan's military leaders had hoped to create a **New Order** in East Asia comprised of Japan, Manchuria, and China. Part of Japan's plan was to seize Soviet Siberia, with its rich resources. In the late 1930s, Japan began to cooperate with Nazi Germany. Japan <u>assumed</u> the two countries would launch an attack on the Soviet Union and divide Soviet resources between them. When Germany signed a nonaggression pact with the Soviets, Japanese leaders were forced to turn to Southeast Asia to find the raw materials they needed to fuel their military machine. A move into Southeast Asia, however, would risk war with Europe and the United States. In the summer of 1940, Japan demanded the right to exploit economic resources in French Indochina. The United States objected. It warned Japan that it would apply economic **sanctions** (restrictions intended to enforce international law) unless Japan withdrew from the area. Japan badly needed the oil and scrap iron it was getting from the United States. Japan was now caught in a dilemma. To gain access to the raw materials it wanted in Southeast Asia, Japan had to risk losing raw materials from the United States. After much debate, Japan decided to launch a surprise attack on U.S. and European colonies in Southeast Asia.

Academic Vocabulary
assume: to believe that something is true even if it has not been stated directly; suppose (p. 539)

7. When Germany signed the nonaggression pact with the Soviets, what dilemma did this create for Japan?

_____

_____

_____

_____

_____

Reading Essentials and Study Guide

Chapter 11, Section 2

For use with textbook pages 541–550

THE COURSE OF WORLD WAR II

CONTENT VOCABULARY
blitzkrieg German for "lightning war," a swift and sudden military attack; used by the Germans during World War II *(page 542)*
partisan a resistance fighter in World War II *(page 550)*

DRAWING FROM EXPERIENCE

Have you ever heard of D-Day, V-E Day, and V-J Day? What happened on these days?

In the last section, you read about the actions of Germany and Japan that led to the beginning of World War II. In this section, you will read about the war itself.

California History Social Science Standards
10.8 Students analyze the causes and consequences of World War II.
Focuses on: 10.8.3, 10.8.4, 10.8.6

ORGANIZING YOUR THOUGHTS

Use the diagram below to help you take notes. During World War II, the major countries of the world were divided into two coalitions, the Grand Alliance (or Allies) and the Axis powers. Identify the three Axis powers and the three major Allies.

Axis Powers

1.
2.
3.

"Big Three" Allies

4.
5.
6.

Reading Essentials and Study Guide

Chapter 11, Section 2 *(continued)*

READ TO LEARN

• Europe at War *(page 542)*

Hitler stunned Europe with the speed of his attack on Poland. His **blitzkrieg,** or "lightning war," used panzer divisions, supported by airplanes. Each panzer division was a strike force of about three hundred tanks with accompanying forces and supplies. Within four weeks, Poland had surrendered. On September 28, 1939, Germany and the Soviet Union divided Poland.

Hitler attacked again on April 9, 1940, with a blitzkrieg against Denmark and Norway. On May 10, Germany launched an attack on the Netherlands, Belgium, and France. The Germans split the Allied armies, trapping French troops and the entire British army on the beaches of Dunkirk. The British managed to evacuate 338,000 Allied troops through the heroic efforts of the Royal Navy and civilians in private boats.

The French signed an armistice on June 22. German armies now occupied about three-fifths of France. An authoritarian regime under German control was set up over the rest of the country. It was known as Vichy France. It was led by an aged French hero from World War I, Marshal Henri Petain. Germany was now in control of western and central Europe, but Britain had still not been defeated. After Dunkirk, the British appealed to the United States for help.

The United States followed a strict policy of <u>isolationism</u>. Laws passed in the 1930s prevented the United States from taking sides or becoming involved in any European wars. President Franklin D. Roosevelt was convinced that the <u>neutrality</u> acts actually encouraged Axis aggression and wanted the acts repealed. The laws were gradually relaxed as the United States supplied food, ships, planes, and weapons to Britain.

Hitler realized that an invasion of Britain could only succeed if Germany gained control of the air. At the beginning of August 1940, the Luftwaffe—the German air force—launched a major offensive. German planes bombed British bases, harbors, communication centers, and war industries. The British fought back. But by the end of August, the British air force had suffered critical losses. In retaliation for a British attack on Berlin, the Luftwaffe began bombing British cities instead of military targets. Instead of demoralizing the British people, this allowed the British air force to rebuild quickly. The British were able to inflict major losses on Luftwaffe bombers. At the end of September, Hitler postponed the invasion of Britain <u>indefinitely</u>.

Hitler was convinced that Britain was remaining in the war only because it expected Soviet support. He thought that if the Soviet Union could be smashed, Britain's last hope would be eliminated. Hitler's invasion of the Soviet Union was scheduled for the spring of 1941, but the attack was delayed because of problems in the Balkans. Mussolini's invasion of Greece had failed in 1940. To secure his southern flank, Hitler seized Greece and Yugoslavia in April 1941.

Academic Vocabulary
isolationism: a policy of national isolation by not forming alliances or other international political and economic relations (p. 543)

Academic Vocabulary
neutrality: remaining impartial by refusing to participate in a war between other powers (p. 543)

Academic Vocabulary
indefinite: not precise; vaguely (p. 543)

Reading Essentials and Study Guide

Chapter 11, Section 2 *(continued)*

On June 22, 1941, Hitler invaded the Soviet Union. German troops advanced rapidly, capturing two million Russian soldiers. However, an early winter and fierce Soviet resistance stopped the Germans. The Germans had no winter uniforms, because they had originally planned to invade in the spring. For the first time in the war, the German armies had been stopped.

7. What prevented Roosevelt from responding to British appeals for help in 1940?

_____

_____

_____

• Japan at War *(page 544)*

On December 7, 1941, Japanese aircraft attacked the U.S. naval base at Pearl Harbor in the Hawaiian Islands. The same day, the Japanese also began assaults on the Philippines and advanced toward the British colony of Malaya. Soon after, the Japanese invaded the Dutch East Indies and occupied a number of islands in the Pacific Ocean. By the spring of 1942, almost all of Southeast Asia and much of the western Pacific were in Japanese hands. Japan now declared the creation of a community of nations. The name given to this new "community" was the Greater East-Asia Co-Prosperity Sphere. The entire region would now be under Japanese direction. Japan also announced its intention to liberate the colonial areas of Southeast Asia from Western rule. For the time being, however, Japan needed the resources of the region for its war machine, and it treated the countries under its rule as conquered lands.

Japanese leaders had hoped that their attack on American bases would destroy the U.S. fleet in the Pacific. They also thought that the Roosevelt administration would accept Japanese domination of the Pacific. But the Japanese miscalculated. The attack on Pearl Harbor unified American opinion about becoming involved in the war. The United States now joined with European nations and Nationalist China in an effort to defeat Japan. Hitler quickly declared war against the United States. Another European conflict had turned into a global war.

8. When the Japanese attacked American bases, what did they hope to accomplish? Were their ideas correct?

_____

_____

_____

Reading Essentials and Study Guide

Chapter 11, Section 2 (continued)

- ### The Allies Advance (page 546)

The entry of the Americans into the war created a new coalition, the Grand Alliance. The three major Allies—Great Britain, the United States, and the Soviet Union—agreed to stress military operations and ignore political differences. At the beginning of 1943, the Allies agreed to fight until the Axis Powers—Germany, Italy, and Japan—surrendered unconditionally.

Defeat was far from Hitler's mind. In North Africa, German forces under General Erwin Rommel broke through the British defenses in Egypt and advanced toward Alexandria. A new German offensive in the Soviet Union led to the capture of the entire Crimea in the spring of 1942. But by the fall of 1942, the war had turned against the Germans. In North Africa, British forces had stopped Rommel's troops at El Alamein in the summer of 1942. In November 1942, British and American forces invaded French North Africa and forced the German and Italian troops there to surrender in May 1943. On the Eastern front, against the advice of his generals, Hitler decided that Stalingrad should be taken. Between November 1942 and February 2, 1943, the Soviets launched a counterattack. German troops were stopped and then encircled. Supply lines were cut off, in frigid winter conditions. The Germans were forced to surrender at Stalingrad. The entire German Sixth Army, considered the best of the German troops, was lost.

In 1942, the tide of battle in the East changed dramatically. In the Battle of the Coral Sea in May 1942, American naval forces stopped the Japanese. The turning point of the war in Asia came on June 4, at the Battle of Midway Island. U.S. planes destroyed four Japanese aircraft carriers. The United States defeated the Japanese navy and established naval superiority in the Pacific. By the fall of 1942, Allied forces in Asia were gathering for two operations. One, commanded by U.S. general Douglas MacArthur, would move into the Philippines through New Guinea and the South Pacific Islands. The other would move across the Pacific with a combination of U.S. Army, Marine, and Navy attacks on Japanese-held islands. The policy was to capture some Japanese-held islands and bypass others, "island hopping" up to Japan.

9. What was the turning point of the war in Asia?

_____

_____

- ### Last Years of the War (page 549)

By the beginning of 1943, the war had turned against Germany, Italy, and Japan. The Allies carried the war to Italy. After taking Sicily, Allied troops began an invasion of mainland Italy in September. After the fall of Sicily, German forces were forced to move in and occupy much of Italy. The Germans set up new defensive lines in the hills south of Rome. The Allied advance up the Italian Peninsula was difficult, with very heavy casualties.

Reading Essentials and Study Guide

Chapter 11, Section 2 *(continued)*

Rome did not fall to the Allies until June 4, 1944. By that time, the Italian war had assumed a secondary role, as the Allied forces opened their "second front" in western Europe.

On June 6, 1944, Allied forces under U.S. general Dwight D. Eisenhower landed on the Normandy beaches of France. Within three months, the Allies had landed two million men and a half-million vehicles. Allied forces then pushed inland and broke through German defensive lines. The Allied troops moved south and east. In Paris, resistance fighters rose up against the occupying Germans. The Allies liberated Paris by the end of August. In March 1945, they crossed the Rhine River and advanced into Germany. At the end of April 1945, Allied armies in northern Germany moved toward the Elbe River, where they linked up with the Soviets.

The Soviets had come a long way since the Battle of Stalingrad in 1943. In July, the Soviets defeated German forces at the Battle of Kursk, the greatest tank battle of World War II. Soviet forces now began advancing westward. They had reoccupied Ukraine by the end of 1943 and moved into the Baltic states by the beginning of 1944. In the north, Soviet troops occupied Warsaw in January 1945 and entered Berlin in April. In the south, Soviet troops swept through Hungary, Romania, and Bulgaria.

By January 1945, Adolf Hitler had moved into a bunker under the city of Berlin to direct the final stages of the war. Hitler continued to blame the Jews for the war. He committed suicide on April 30, two days after Mussolini had been shot by Italian **partisans** (resistance fighters). On May 7, 1945, German commanders surrendered. The war in Europe was finally over.

The war in Asia continued. Beginning in 1943, U.S. forces had gone on the offensive and advanced, slowly at times, across the Pacific. There was a new U.S. president, Harry S Truman, who had become president on the death of Roosevelt in April. Truman had a difficult decision to make. Should he use newly developed atomic weapons to bring the war to an end or find another way to defeat the Japanese forces? Truman decided to use the bombs. The first bomb was dropped on the Japanese city of Hiroshima on August 6, 1945. Three days later, a second bomb was dropped on Nagasaki. Both cities were leveled. Thousands of people died immediately after the bombs were dropped. Thousands more died in later months from radiation. Japan surrendered on August 14.

World War II was finally over. Seventeen million had died in battle. Perhaps 20 million civilians had died as well. Some estimates place total losses at 50 million.

10. How did President Truman bring the war to an end?

_____

_____

Reading Essentials and Study Guide

Chapter 11, Section 3

For use with textbook pages 551–557

THE NEW ORDER AND THE HOLOCAUST

CONTENT VOCABULARY

genocide the deliberate mass murder of a racial, political, or cultural group *(page 553)*

collaborator a person who assists the enemy *(page 556)*

DRAWING FROM EXPERIENCE

Have you ever heard about the Holocaust? Have you ever been to the Holocaust Museum in Washington, D.C.? What was the Holocaust? Why did it take place?

In the last two sections, you learned about events leading to World War II and the battles of the war. In this section, you will learn about the atrocities committed by the Nazis and the Japanese against the peoples they conquered.

> **California History Social Science Standards**
>
> **10.8** Students analyze the causes and consequences of World War II.
>
> **Focuses on:**
> 10.8.5, 10.8.6

ORGANIZING YOUR THOUGHTS

Use the chart below to help you take notes. Describe the following policies or programs of Hitler and the Nazis.

Nazi Policy	Description
resettlement	1.
forced labor	2.
Final Solution	3.
Einsatzgruppen	4.
death camps	5.

Reading Essentials and Study Guide

Chapter 11, Section 3 *(continued)*

READ TO LEARN

• The New Order in Europe *(page 552)*

In 1942, the Nazi regime stretched across Europe from the English Channel in the west to the outskirts of Moscow in the east. Nazi-occupied Europe was mainly organized in one of two ways. Some areas were annexed by Nazi Germany and made into German provinces. In other areas, German military or civilian officials would run the area with help from local people who were willing to collaborate with the Nazis. In the conquered lands to the east, the Nazis were especially ruthless. These lands were seen as "living space" for German expansion. Hitler began to <u>implement</u> his racial program soon after the conquest of Poland. Heinrich Himmler, the leader of the SS, was put in charge of German resettlement plans in the east. His job was to move the Slavic peoples out and replace them with Germans. One million Poles were forced to move to southern Poland. By 1942, two million ethnic Germans had been settled in Poland.

Academic Vocabulary
implement: to begin or carry out a plan or course of action (p. 552)

Labor shortages in Germany led to a policy of rounding up foreign workers. By the summer of 1944, seven million Europeans were working in Germany. Another seven million people were forced to work for the Nazis in their own countries, sometimes in military camps. In the end, the use of forced labor caused problems for Germany. Sending so many workers to Germany disrupted industrial production in the occupied countries that could have helped Germany. The brutal way that Germany recruited foreign workers led more and more people to resist the Nazi occupation forces.

6. How did the use of forced labor cause problems for Germany?

_____

_____

_____

_____

• The Holocaust *(page 553)*

No aspect of the Nazi New Order was more terrifying than the deliberate attempt to exterminate the Jews. Racial struggle was a key element in Hitler's ideas. To him, racial struggle was a clearly defined conflict of opposites. On one side were the Aryans, creators of human cultural development. On the other side were the Jews, parasites, in Hitler's view, who were trying to destroy the Aryans. The SS had responsibility for what the Nazis called their Final Solution to the Jewish problem. The Final Solution was **genocide,** the physical extermination of all Jews. Reinhard Heydrich, head of the SS's

Reading Essentials and Study Guide

Chapter 11, Section 3 *(continued)*

Security Service, was given the task of administering the Final Solution. Heydrich created special strike forces, called *Einsatzgruppen*, to carry out Nazi plans. After the defeat of Poland, he ordered these forces to round up all Polish Jews and put them in ghettos in a number of Polish cities. Conditions were horrible in these ghettos. Despite the suffering, the people in the ghettos tried to <u>adjust</u>, and some ghettos organized resistance against the Nazis. In June 1941, the strike forces were given the new job of acting as mobile killing units. These SS death squads followed the regular army's advance into the Soviet Union. Their job was to round up Jews in their villages, execute them, and bury them in mass graves. The graves were often giant pits dug by the victims themselves before they were shot.

Academic Vocabulary
adjust: to conform to fit into a new place or situation (p. 553)

Although these strike forces killed over one million Jews, this was not enough for the Nazi leaders. They decided to kill the European Jewish population in death camps. Beginning in 1942, Jews from occupied countries were shipped to one of six extermination centers that had been built in Poland. Auschwitz was the largest of these centers. By the spring of 1942, the death camps were in full operation.

The Germans killed between five and six million Jews, over three million of them in the death camps. Virtually 90 percent of the Jewish populations of Poland, the Baltic countries, and Germany were killed. Overall, the Holocaust was responsible for the death of nearly two-thirds of European Jews. The Nazis were also responsible for the death by shooting, starvation, or overwork of at least another nine to ten million non-Jewish people. The Nazis considered the Gypsies of Europe, like the Jews, to be a race containing alien blood. The Gypsies were rounded up for mass killing. About 40 percent of Europe's one million Gypsies were killed in the death camps. The leading citizens of the Slavic peoples—the clergy, intellectuals, civil leaders, judges, and lawyers—were arrested and killed. Another four million Poles, Ukrainians, and Belorussians lost their lives as slave laborers for Nazi Germany. Finally, at least three million to four million Soviet prisoners of war were killed in captivity.

This mass slaughter of European civilians, particularly European Jews, is known as the Holocaust. Jews in and out of the camps tried to resist the Nazis. Some were helped by friends and even strangers, hidden in villages or smuggled into safe areas. Foreign diplomats tried to save Jews by issuing exit visas. The nation of Denmark saved almost its entire Jewish population.

Some people did not believe the stories about the death camps. This was partly because the Allies in World War I had exaggerated German atrocities to create enthusiasm for the war. Other people pretended not to notice what was happening. Even worse, **collaborators** (people who assisted the enemy) helped the Nazis hunt down Jews. The Allies were aware of the concentration camps and death camps but chose to concentrate on ending the war. Not until after the war did they learn the full extent of the horror and inhumanity of the Holocaust.

Reading Essentials and Study Guide

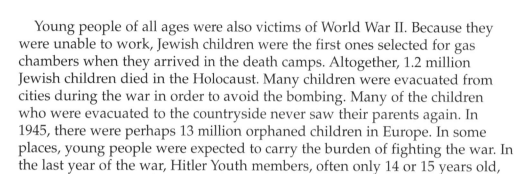

Chapter 11, Section 3 *(continued)*

Young people of all ages were also victims of World War II. Because they were unable to work, Jewish children were the first ones selected for gas chambers when they arrived in the death camps. Altogether, 1.2 million Jewish children died in the Holocaust. Many children were evacuated from cities during the war in order to avoid the bombing. Many of the children who were evacuated to the countryside never saw their parents again. In 1945, there were perhaps 13 million orphaned children in Europe. In some places, young people were expected to carry the burden of fighting the war. In the last year of the war, Hitler Youth members, often only 14 or 15 years old, could be found in the front lines.

7. Why did the Holocaust continue until the end of the war?

_____

_____

_____

_____

- ## The New Order in Asia *(page 557)*

Japanese war policy in occupied Asia was basically defensive. Japan hoped to use the occupied territories to meet its need for raw materials. These territories would also be a market for Japanese manufactured goods. To organize these territories, Japanese leaders included them in the Greater East-Asia Co-Prosperity Sphere. The Japanese had conquered Southeast Asia under the slogan "Asia for the Asiatics." Japanese officials in occupied territories quickly made contact with anticolonialists. They promised the people that local governments would be established. Such governments were eventually set up in Burma, the Dutch East Indies, Vietnam, and the Philippines.

In fact, real power rested with Japanese military authorities in each territory. In turn, the local Japanese military command was under the authority of the Army General Staff in Tokyo. The economic resources of the colonies were used for the benefit of the Japanese war machine. The native peoples in occupied lands were recruited to serve in local military units or were forced to work on public works projects. In some cases, these policies brought severe hardships to peoples living in the occupied areas. In Vietnam, for example, local Japanese authorities forcibly took rice and shipped it abroad. This led directly to a food shortage that caused over a million Vietnamese to starve to death in 1944 and 1945.

At first, many Southeast Asian nationalists took Japanese promises at face value and agreed to cooperate with their new masters. Eventually, the nature of Japanese occupation policies became clear, and sentiment turned against Japan.

Reading Essentials and Study Guide

Chapter 11, Section 3 *(continued)*

Japanese officials provoked negative reactions by their arrogance and contempt for local customs. In the Dutch East Indies, for example, Indonesians were required to bow in the direction of Tokyo and to recognize the divinity of the Japanese emperor. In Burma, Buddhist pagodas were used as military latrines.

In construction projects to help their war effort, the Japanese made extensive use of labor forces composed of both prisoners of war and local peoples. In building the Burma-Thailand railway in 1943, for example, the Japanese used 61,000 Australian, British, and Dutch prisoners of war and almost 300,000 workers from Burma, Malaya, Thailand, and the Dutch East Indies. An inadequate diet and appalling work conditions in an unhealthy climate led to the death of 12,000 Allied prisoners of war and 90,000 workers by the time the railway was completed.

Indonesian patriots tried to have it both ways. They pretended to support Japan while actually sabotaging the Japanese administration. In French Indochina, Ho Chi Minh's Communist Party made contact with U.S. military units in South China. The Communists agreed to provide information on Japanese troop movements and to rescue downed American fliers in the area. By the end of the war, little support remained in the region for the Japanese "liberators."

8. How did the Japanese gain the support of people in occupied territories? Why did they eventually lose this support?

_____

_____

_____

_____

_____

Glencoe World History—Modern Times

Reading Essentials and Study Guide

Chapter 11, Section 4

For use with textbook pages 558–565

THE HOME FRONT AND THE AFTERMATH OF THE WAR

CONTENT VOCABULARY

mobilization the process of assembling troops and supplies and making them ready for war *(page 559)*

kamikaze Japanese for "divine wind," a suicide mission in which Japanese pilots flew their airplanes into U.S. fighting ships *(page 561)*

DRAWING FROM EXPERIENCE

Have you heard of the "iron curtain"? What does this describe? Who first used this term?

In the last three sections, you learned about events before and during World War II. In this section, you will learn about events immediately following the war. You will also learn how the war affected civilians in Europe, the United States, and Japan.

California History Social Science Standards

10.8 Students analyze the causes and consequences of World War II.
10.9 Students analyze the international developments in the post-World War II world.

Focuses on:
10.8.3, 10.8.4, 10.9.1

ORGANIZING YOUR THOUGHTS

Use the chart below to help you take notes. Describe how the populations of Germany, Japan, the Soviet Union, and the United States were mobilized for war.

Country	Mobilization
Soviet Union	1.
United States	2.
Germany	3.
Japan	4.

Reading Essentials and Study Guide

Chapter 11, Section 4 (continued)

READ TO LEARN

• The Mobilization of Peoples: Four Examples (page 559)

World War II had an enormous <u>impact</u> on civilian life in the Soviet Union, the United States, Germany, and Japan. Even more than World War I, World War II was a total war. Fighting was much more widespread and covered most of the world. Economic **mobilization** (the act of assembling and preparing for war) was more extensive. The mobilization of women was also greater. The number of civilians killed—almost twenty million—was far higher. Many of these victims were children.

The initial defeats of the Soviet Union led to drastic emergency measures that affected the lives of the civilian population. Leningrad, for example, experienced nine hundred days of siege. Its people became so desperate for food that they ate dogs, cats, and mice. Probably 1.5 million people died in the city. As the German army advanced into Soviet territory, Soviet workers dismantled and shipped the factories in the western part of the Soviet Union to the interior. This "battle of machines" produced 78,000 tanks and 98,000 artillery pieces. Soviet women played a major role in the war effort. Women and girls worked in industries, mines, and railroads. The Soviet Union was the only country in World War II to use women in battle.

The home front in the United States was different. The United States was not fighting the war in its own territory. Eventually, the United States became the arsenal of the Allied Powers. It produced much of the military equipment the Allies needed. At the height of war production in November 1943, the country was building six ships a day and 96,000 planes per year.

The mobilization of the American economy resulted in some social turmoil, however. The construction of new factories created boomtowns. Thousands of people, many of them women, came there to work but then faced a shortage of houses and schools. Widespread movements of people took place. Sixteen million men and women were enrolled in the military and moved frequently. Another 16 million, mostly wives and girlfriends of servicemen or workers looking for jobs, also moved around the country.

Over a million African Americans moved from the rural South to the cities of the North and West, looking for jobs. The presence of African Americans in areas where they had not lived before led to racial tensions and sometimes even racial riots. One million African Americans enrolled in the military, but they were segregated in their own battle units. Angered by the way they were treated, some became militant and prepared to fight for their civil rights. Japanese Americans faced even more serious problems. On the West Coast, 110,000 Japanese Americans were moved to camps surrounded by barbed wire. They were required to take loyalty oaths, even though 65 percent of them had been born in the United States. Public officials claimed this policy was necessary for security reasons.

Academic Vocabulary
impact: a significant or major effect (p. 559)

Reading Essentials and Study Guide

Chapter 11, Section 4 *(continued)*

In Germany, Hitler was well aware of the importance of the home front. He believed that the collapse of the home front in World War I had caused Germany's defeat. In his determination to keep this from happening again, he adopted economic policies that may have cost Germany the war. To maintain morale during the first two years of the war, Hitler refused to cut consumer goods production or to increase the production of armaments. After German defeats on the Russian front and the American entry into the war, Hitler finally ordered a massive increase in armaments production and in the size of the army. Albert Speer, the minister for armaments and munitions, tripled the production of armaments between 1942 and 1943, despite Allied air raids. A total mobilization of the economy was put into effect in July 1944. Schools, theaters, and cafes were closed. By that time, though, total war mobilization was too late to save Germany from defeat.

Nazi attitudes toward women changed over the course of the war. Before the war, the Nazis had worked to keep women out of the job market. As the war progressed and more and more men were called up for military service, these attitudes changed. Nazi magazines now proclaimed, "We see the woman as the eternal mother of our people, but also as the working and fighting comrade of the man." In spite of this change, the number of women working in industry, agriculture, commerce, and domestic service increased only slightly. Many women, especially those of the middle class, did not want jobs, particularly in factories.

Wartime Japan was a highly mobilized society. To guarantee its control over all national resources, the government created a planning board to control prices, wages, labor, and resources. Citizens were encouraged to sacrifice their resources, and sometimes their lives, for the national cause. Young Japanese were encouraged to volunteer to serve as pilots in suicide missions against the American ships. These pilots were known as **kamikaze,** or "divine wind."

Japan was extremely reluctant to mobilize women on behalf of Japan's war effort. General Hideki Tojo, prime minister from 1941 to 1944, opposed female employment. Female employment increased during the war, but only in such areas as the textile industry and farming, where women had traditionally worked. Instead of using women to meet labor shortages, the Japanese government brought in Korean and Chinese laborers as an <u>alternative</u>.

Academic Vocabulary
alternative: something that can be chosen instead of something else (p. 561)

5. How were women used in the war effort in Germany, Japan, the Soviet Union, and the United States?

_____

_____

_____

_____

Reading Essentials and Study Guide

Chapter 11, Section 4 (continued)

- ### Frontline Civilians: The Bombing of Cities (page 562)

Bombing was used in World War II against military targets, enemy troops, and civilian populations. The bombing of civilians in World War II made the home front a dangerous place. The first sustained use of civilian bombing began in early September 1940 in Great Britain. For months, the German air force bombed London nightly. Thousands of civilians were killed or injured, and enormous damage was done. Nevertheless, Londoners' morale remained high. The blitz, as the British called the German air raids, soon became a national experience. The blitz was carried to many other British cities and towns. The ability of Londoners to maintain their morale set the standard for the rest of the British population. The theory that the bombing of civilian targets would force peace was proved wrong. The British failed to learn from their own experience, however. Churchill and his advisers believed that destroying German communities would break civilian morale and bring victory. Major bombing raids on German cities began in 1942.

Bombing raids added an element of terror to circumstances that were already difficult because of shortages of food, clothing, and fuel. Germans especially feared the incendiary bombs, which created firestorms that swept through cities. The bombing of Dresden from February 13 to 15, 1945, created a firestorm that may have killed as many as 100,000 people. Germany suffered enormously from the Allied bombing raids. Millions of buildings were destroyed, and possibly 500,000 civilians died. But the bombings did not destroy Germany's industrial capacity. Production of war materials actually increased between 1942 and 1944, despite the bombing. However, the widespread destruction of transportation systems and fuel supplies made it very difficult for the new materials to reach the German military.

In Japan, the bombing of civilians reached a new level with the use of the first atomic bomb. Japan was open to air raids toward the end of the war because its air force had almost been destroyed. Attacks on Japanese cities by the new U.S. B-29 Superfortresses had begun on November 24, 1944. By the summer of 1945, many of Japan's industries had been destroyed, along with one-fourth of its dwellings. The Japanese government decreed the mobilization of all people between the ages of 13 and 60 into a People's Volunteer Corps. Fearing high U.S. casualties in a land invasion of Japan, President Truman and his advisers decided to drop the atomic bomb on Hiroshima and Nagasaki in August 1945.

6. What was the theory behind the bombing of civilians? Did this theory prove to be right or wrong?

_____

_____

_____

Reading Essentials and Study Guide

Chapter 11, Section 4 *(continued)*

• Peace and a New War *(page 564)*

The end of World War II was followed by a period of political tensions, known as the **Cold War.** The Cold War was primarily an ideological conflict between the United States and the Soviet Union, but it dominated world affairs until the end of the 1980s.

Stalin, Roosevelt, and Churchill were the leaders of the Grand Alliance. They met at Tehran in November 1943 to decide the future course of the war. Their major decision concerned the final assault on Germany. Stalin and Roosevelt argued for an American-British invasion through France. This was scheduled for the spring of 1944. This plan had important consequences. It meant that Soviet and British-American forces would meet in Germany along a north-south dividing line. Soviet forces would liberate Eastern Europe. The Allies also agreed to a partition of postwar Germany.

The Big Three powers met again at Yalta in southern Russia in February 1945. By then, the defeat of Germany was obvious. The Western powers were now faced with the reality that 11 million Soviet soldiers were taking possession of Eastern and much of Central Europe. Stalin was very suspicious of the Western powers. He wanted a buffer to protect the Soviet Union from future Western aggression. This would mean establishing pro-Soviet governments along the border of the Soviet Union. Roosevelt, however, favored the idea of self-determination for Europe. He wanted to help liberated Europe create "democratic institutions of their own choice." Liberated countries would hold free elections to determine their political systems.

At Yalta, Roosevelt wanted Soviet military help against Japan. Roosevelt agreed to Stalin's price for military aid against Japan. Stalin wanted Sakhalin and the Kuril Islands, which were ruled by Japan. He also wanted two warm-water ports and railroad rights in Manchuria. Roosevelt also wanted the Big Three powers to pledge to be part of an international organization devoted to peacefully resolving international conflicts. Both Churchill and Stalin accepted Roosevelt's plans for the United Nations and set the first meeting for San Francisco in April 1945.

Differences over Germany and Eastern Europe were treated less decisively. The Big Three reaffirmed that Germany must surrender unconditionally. It would be divided into four zones, which would be occupied and governed by the military forces of the United States, Great Britain, France, and the Soviet Union. A compromise was also worked out in regard to Poland. Stalin agreed to free elections in the future to determine a new government in that country. The issue of free elections in Eastern Europe caused a serious split between the Soviets and the Americans. This soon became evident at the next conference of the Big Three powers at Potsdam, Germany.

The Potsdam conference of July 1945 began under a cloud of mistrust. Roosevelt had died on April 12 and had been succeeded by Harry Truman. At Potsdam, Truman demanded free elections in Eastern Europe. Stalin objected.

Reading Essentials and Study Guide

Chapter 11, Section 4 (continued)

He wanted absolute military security. To him, this security could be gained only by the presence of Communist states in Eastern Europe.

The war had ended, but a new struggle was already beginning. Many in the West thought Soviet policy was part of a worldwide Communist conspiracy. The Soviets viewed Western, and especially American, policy as nothing less than global capitalist expansionism. In March 1946, in a speech, the former British prime minister Winston Churchill declared that "an iron curtain" had "descended across the continent," dividing Europe into two hostile camps. Stalin called Churchill's speech a "call to war with the Soviet Union." Only months after World War II had ended, the world was bitterly divided again.

7. Why did Stalin object to free elections in Eastern Europe?

_____

_____

_____

_____

_____

Reading Essentials and Study Guide

Chapter 12, Section 1

For use with textbook pages 583–589

DEVELOPMENT OF THE COLD WAR

CONTENT VOCABULARY

satellite state a country that is economically and politically dependent on another country *(page 585)*

policy of containment a plan to keep something, such as communism, within its existing geographical boundaries and prevent further aggressive moves *(page 585)*

arms race the build-up of armies and huge arsenals of nuclear weapons and missiles by the United States and the Soviet Union *(page 586)*

deterrence security policy which holds that if two sides in a political conflict have huge arsenals of nuclear weapons, war can be prevented *(page 587)*

domino theory the belief held by U.S. policymakers that if the Communists succeeded in South Vietnam, other countries in Asia would fall (like dominoes) to communism *(page 589)*

DRAWING FROM EXPERIENCE

Which countries of the world would you consider to be superpowers today? Why do you think so?

In this section, you will learn about the period of conflict called the Cold War that developed between the United States and the Soviet Union after the end of World War II.

ORGANIZING YOUR THOUGHTS

Use the chart below to help you take notes. During the Cold War period, new military alliances were created. Identify the members of the alliances in the chart below.

Alliance	Members
NATO	1.
Warsaw Pact	2.
SEATO	3.
CENTO	4.

> **California History Social Science Standards**
>
> **10.9** Students analyze the international developments in the post-World War II world.
>
> **Focuses on:**
> 10.9.2, 10.9.3, 10.9.8

Reading Essentials and Study Guide

Chapter 12, Section 1 (continued)

READ TO LEARN

- ## Confrontation of the Superpowers (page 584)

After World War II, the United States and the Soviet Union soon became rivals. U.S. leaders still feared communism, and Stalin still feared the capitalist West. Between 1945 and 1949, the two superpowers (countries whose military power is combined with political influence) began to oppose each other. The Soviet government was not willing to give up its control of Eastern Europe. American leaders were not willing to give up the power and prestige the United States had gained throughout the world.

The United States and Great Britain believed that the nations of Eastern Europe should freely determine their own governments. Stalin opposed their plans. The Soviet army had freed Eastern Europe from the Nazis, and it stayed in these countries after the war.

Greece was another area of disagreement between the superpowers. In 1946, the Communist People's Liberation Army fought anticommunist forces for control of Greece. Great Britain supported the anticommunist forces. However, economic problems in Britain forced the British to withdraw its aid from Greece. U.S. President Harry Truman responded to the British withdrawal by issuing the Truman Doctrine. The Truman Doctrine stated that the United States would provide money to countries (such as Greece) that were threatened by Communist expansion. By 1947, the split in Europe between the United States and the Soviet Union had become a fact of life. The United States adopted a **policy of containment** to keep communism within its existing boundaries and prevent further Soviet aggression.

Academic Vocabulary
aid: to give assistance (p. 584)

The European Recovery Program followed the Truman Doctrine in June 1947. It is better known as the Marshall Plan. The goal of the program was to rebuild the prosperity and stability of Europe. It included $13 billion in aid for Europe's economic recovery. The Marshall Plan was based on the belief that Communist aggression was successful in countries that had economic problems. The Marshall Plan was not meant to shut out the Soviet Union or its Eastern European **satellite states** (states that are economically and politically dependent on a larger, more powerful state). But they refused to participate. The Soviets saw the Marshall Plan as an attempt to buy the support of countries. In 1949, the Soviet Union responded to the Marshall Plan by founding the Council for Mutual Economic Assistance (COMECON) to help the Eastern European states. COMECON largely failed, however, because the Soviet Union was unable to provide much financial aid.

Germany was also an area of disagreement between the Soviets and the West. At the end of the war, the Allied Powers had divided Germany into four zones. Each zone was occupied by one of the Allies (the United States, the Soviet Union, Great Britain, and France). Berlin was also divided into four zones. By 1948, Great Britain, France, and the United States were making plans to unify the three Western sections of Germany into a West German

Academic Vocabulary
occupy: to take or hold possession or control of (p. 585)

Reading Essentials and Study Guide

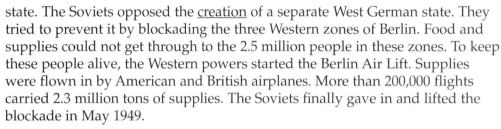

Chapter 12, Section 1 *(continued)*

state. The Soviets opposed the <u>creation</u> of a separate West German state. They tried to prevent it by blockading the three Western zones of Berlin. Food and supplies could not get through to the 2.5 million people in these zones. To keep these people alive, the Western powers started the Berlin Air Lift. Supplies were flown in by American and British airplanes. More than 200,000 flights carried 2.3 million tons of supplies. The Soviets finally gave in and lifted the blockade in May 1949.

In September 1949, the Federal Republic of Germany (or West Germany) was created. Its capital was Bonn. Less than a month later, a separate East German state, the German Democratic Republic, was set up by the Soviets. East Berlin was its capital.

Academic Vocabulary
creation: the act of making, inventing, or producing (p. 585)

5. What was the Marshall Plan?

_____

_____

_____

_____

- **Spread of the Cold War** *(page 586)*

In 1949, Chinese Communists took control of the government of China. This added to U.S. fears about the spread of communism. The Soviet Union also exploded its first atomic bomb in 1949. The United States and the Soviet Union were soon involved in an **arms race,** in which both countries built up their armies and weapons. In the early 1950s, the Soviet Union and the United States developed the even more deadly hydrogen bomb. By the mid-1950s, both nations had intercontinental ballistic missiles that could send bombs anywhere. Both sides believed that they needed arsenals of nuclear weapons to prevent war. They believed that neither side would launch a nuclear attack, because the other side would be able to strike back with its nuclear weapons. In 1957, the Soviets sent *Sputnik I,* the first human-made space satellite, to orbit the earth. Americans began to fear that the Soviet Union had a huge lead in building missiles.

The need for security during the Cold War led to the formation of new military alliances. The North Atlantic Treaty Organization (NATO) was formed in April 1949. Belgium, Luxembourg, France, the Netherlands, Great Britain, Italy, Denmark, Norway, Portugal, and Iceland signed a treaty with the United States and Canada. All of these nations agreed to help each other if any of them was attacked. A few years later, West Germany, Turkey, and Greece joined NATO. In 1955, the Soviet Union formed an alliance with Albania, Bulgaria, Czechoslovakia, East Germany, Hungary, Poland, and Romania. This alliance was known as the Warsaw Pact. To stop Soviet aggression in the East, the United States, Great Britain, France, Pakistan, Thailand, the Philippines,

Reading Essentials and Study Guide

Chapter 12, Section 1 (continued)

Australia, and New Zealand formed the Southeast Asia Treaty Organization (SEATO). To prevent the Soviet Union from expanding to the south, Turkey, Iraq, Iran, Pakistan, Great Britain, and the United States formed the Central Treaty Organization (CENTO). By the mid-1950s, the United States was allied militarily with 42 states around the world.

Berlin was still divided into two parts, a reminder of the division of West and East. West Berlin was far more prosperous than East Berlin and East Germany. Many East Germans escaped their country by fleeing through West Berlin. Nikita Khrushchev, who became the leader of the Soviet Union in 1955, decided to stop the East Germans from escaping in this way. In August 1961, the East German government began to build a wall separating West Berlin from East Berlin. The Berlin Wall became a symbol of the division between the two superpowers.

The Cold War intensified during the <u>administration</u> of U.S. President John F. Kennedy. In 1959, Fidel Castro overthrew the Cuban dictator Fulgencio Batista and set up a Communist government in Cuba. President Kennedy approved a secret plan for Cuban exiles to invade Cuba in the hope of causing a revolt against Castro. The invasion, called the Bay of Pigs, was a disaster. Many of the exiles were killed or captured.

Academic Vocabulary
administration: the group of political executives who help the President run the country (p. 587)

After the Bay of Pigs, the Soviet Union sent arms and military advisers to Cuba. In 1962, Khrushchev began to place nuclear missiles in Cuba. The United States was not willing to allow nuclear weapons so close to the U.S. mainland. In October 1962, Kennedy found out that Soviet ships carrying missiles were heading to Cuba. He tried to stop them by blockading Cuba. This gave the two sides time to find a peaceful solution. Khrushchev agreed to stop the ships and remove Soviet missiles from Cuba if Kennedy pledged not to invade Cuba. Kennedy quickly agreed.

The Cuban missile crisis had brought the world close to nuclear war. The realization that the world might have been destroyed had a profound influence on both sides. A hotline <u>communications</u> system between Moscow and Washington, D.C. was installed in 1963. The two superpowers could now communicate quickly in times of crisis.

Academic Vocabulary
communication: systems for communicating, like telephones or the Internet (p. 588)

Reading Essentials and Study Guide

Chapter 12, Section 1 (continued)

6. Why did the United States and the Soviet Union become involved in an arms race?

_____

_____

_____

_____

• Vietnam and the Domino Theory *(page 589)*

By 1963, the United States had been drawn into a new conflict—the Vietnam War. In 1964, under President Lyndon B. Johnson, more and more U.S. troops were sent to Vietnam. Their purpose was to keep the Communist government of North Vietnam from gaining control of South Vietnam. The United States saw the conflict in terms of a **domino theory.** According to this theory, if the Communists were able to gain control of South Vietnam, other countries in Asia would also fall (like dominoes) to communism.

The United States failed to defeat the determined North Vietnamese. The large number of American troops sent to Vietnam soon produced an antiwar movement in the United States, especially among college students. Richard Nixon was elected president by pledging to stop the war. But ending the war was not easy. Finally, in 1973, President Nixon reached an agreement with the North Vietnamese that allowed the United States to withdraw its troops. Within two years, Communist armies from the North had reunited Vietnam.

The domino theory turned out to be wrong. New nations in Southeast Asia, such as the Phillippines, were able to avoid Communist governments. A split between Communist China and the Soviet Union put an end to the idea that there was single form of communism directed by Moscow. Under President Nixon, American relations with China were reestablished. The Vietnam War showed that there were limits to American power. By the end of the war, a new era in American-Soviet relations had begun.

7. What was the domino theory? Was it right or wrong? Why?

_____

_____

_____

_____

_____

Reading Essentials and Study Guide

Chapter 12, Section 2

For use with textbook pages 592–596

THE SOVIET UNION AND EASTERN EUROPE

CONTENT VOCABULARY

heavy industry the manufacture of machines and equipment for factories and mines *(page 593)*

de-Stalinization the process of eliminating the more ruthless policies of Stalin *(page 593)*

DRAWING FROM EXPERIENCE

What kind of house or apartment do you live in? How many rooms does it have? Do you have your own room?

In the last section, you read about the Cold War between the United States and the Soviet Union. In this section, you will read about the Soviet Union and Eastern Europe during 1950s and 1960s. During this time, the average Russian family lived in a one-room apartment.

> **California History Social Science Standards**
>
> **10.9** Students analyze the international developments in the post-World War II world.
>
> **Focuses on:** 10.9.5, 10.9.7

ORGANIZING YOUR THOUGHTS

Use the diagram below to help you take notes. After World War II, six countries in Eastern Europe became Soviet satellite states. Identify these six countries.

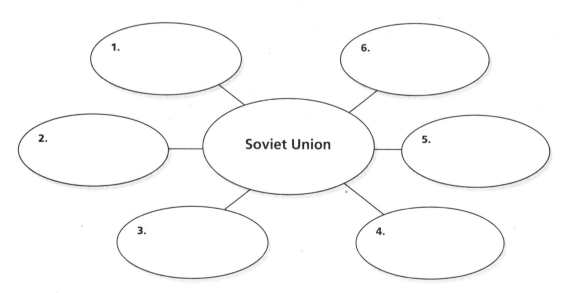

Reading Essentials and Study Guide

Chapter 12, Section 2 *(continued)*

READ TO LEARN

- **Recovery Soviet-Style** *(page 593)*

World War II devastated the Soviet Union. To create a new industrial base after the war, Stalin emphasized the production of goods for export. In some respects, this led to a rapid economic recovery. By 1950, industrial production had surpassed prewar levels by 40 percent. New power plants, canals, and giant factories were built. **Heavy industry** (the manufacture of machines and equipment for factories and mines) increased, mainly for the benefit of the military. But the Soviet people did not benefit from the industrialization. The emphasis on heavy industry meant that not enough consumer goods were produced. The housing shortage was also severe. The average Russian family lived in a one-room apartment.

Stalin was still the master of the Soviet Union. He did not share power and had little respect for other Communist Party leaders. His suspicions and lack of trust caused the repression in the Soviet Union to increase. In 1946, the government decreed that all literary and scientific work had to <u>conform</u> to the political needs of the state.

Academic Vocabulary
conform: to be obedient or compliant (p. 593)

Stalin died in 1953. A group of leaders succeeded him, but Nikita Khrushchev soon emerged as the chief Soviet policy maker. Khrushchev took steps to undo some of the worst features of Stalin's regime. The process of eliminating the more ruthless policies of Stalin became known as **de-Stalinization.** Khrushchev loosened government controls on literary works. In 1962, for example, he allowed the publication of *A Day in the Life of Ivan Denisovich* by Alexander Solzhenitsyn. This book dealt with life in a Siberian forced-labor camp. Many Soviets identified with Ivan as a <u>symbol</u> of the suffering they had endured under Stalin. Khrushchev also placed more emphasis on producing consumer goods. He also tried to increase farm production by growing corn and cultivating lands east of the Ural Mountains. The attempt to increase farm production failed. This failure and the increased military spending hurt the Soviet economy. Foreign policy failures also damaged Khrushchev's reputation. After the Cuban missile crisis, he was voted out of office and forced into retirement.

Academic Vocabulary
symbol: something that stands for something else by reason of relationship, association, or convention; a visible sign of something invisible (p. 594)

Reading Essentials and Study Guide

Chapter 12, Section 2 *(continued)*

7. How did the emphasis on heavy industry affect the Soviet people?

_____

_____

_____

_____

- **Eastern Europe: Behind the Iron Curtain** *(page 594)*

Between 1945 and 1947, Soviet-controlled Communist governments took control of East Germany, Bulgaria, Romania, Poland, and Hungary. In Czechoslovakia, there was a strong tradition of democracy and a multi-party system, so the Soviets did not seize control until 1948. Albania and Yugoslavia were also Communist countries, but the Soviet Union did not control them. During the war, both countries had strong Communist movements that resisted the Nazis. After the war, local Communist parties took control. In Albania, Communists set up a Stalinist-type regime that grew more and more independent of the Soviet Union. In Yugoslavia, Josip Broz, known as Tito, had been the leader of the communist resistance movement. After the war, he worked to create an independent communist state in Yugoslavia. Stalin hoped to gain control of Yugoslavia, but Tito refused to give in to Stalin's demands. Tito ruled Yugoslavia until his death in 1980. Yugoslavia had a communist government, but it was not a Soviet satellite state.

Between 1948 and 1953, the Eastern European satellite states followed the example of the Soviet Union. They had five-year plans, with emphasis on heavy industry rather than consumer goods. They began to collectivize agriculture. They eliminated all noncommunist parties and set up secret police and military forces. But communism did not develop deep roots among the peoples of Eastern Europe. The Soviets exploited Eastern Europe economically and made living conditions hard for most people.

In the 1950s and 1960s, the Soviet Union made it clear that it would not allow its satellite states to become independent of Soviet control. In 1956, protests erupted in Poland. In response, the Polish Communist Party adopted a series of reforms and elected Wladyslaw Gomulka as first secretary. Gomulka declared that Poland had the right to follow its own path. But Poland compromised. It pledged to remain loyal to the Warsaw Pact.

In Hungary, economic problems and unrest led to calls for revolt. To end the rebellion, Imre Nagy, the Hungarian leader, declared that Hungary was a free nation on November 1, 1956. He also promised free elections. Three days after Nagy's declaration, the Soviet army attacked Budapest. The Soviets reestablished control over the country. Nagy was captured by the Soviet military and executed two years later.

Reading Essentials and Study Guide

Chapter 12, Section 2 *(continued)*

In Czechoslovakia, Antonin Novotny had been placed in power in 1953 by Stalin himself. In fact, he was called "Little Stalin." By the late 1960s, Novotny had alienated many members of his own party. Czech writers especially disliked him. A writers' rebellion led to Novotny's resignation in 1968. In January 1968, Alexander Dubćek was elected first secretary of the Communist party. He began a number of reforms, including freedom of speech and press and the freedom to travel abroad. He relaxed censorship and promised to democratize the Czechoslovakian political system. A period of euphoria broke out that became known as the "Prague Spring." In response, the Soviet army invaded Czechoslovakia in August 1968 and crushed the reform movement. Gustav Husák replaced Dubćek, did away with his reforms, and reestablished the old order.

8. Why were Albania and Yugoslavia able to remain free of Soviet control?

_____

_____

_____

_____

_____

Reading Essentials and Study Guide

Chapter 12, Section 3

For use with textbook pages 597–605

WESTERN EUROPE AND NORTH AMERICA

CONTENT VOCABULARY

welfare state a state in which the government takes responsibility for providing citizens with services and a minimal standard of living *(page 599)*

bloc a group of nations with a common purpose *(page 600)*

real wages the actual purchasing power of income *(page 600)*

civil right movement equal rights movement for African Americans beginning in 1954 *(page 601)*

consumer society a society that is preoccupied with buying goods, not producing one *(page 603)*

women's liberation movement late 1960s equal rights movement for women *(page 604)*

DRAWING FROM EXPERIENCE

How do you feel about welfare? Do you think the government has a responsibility to provide citizens with basic needs, such as food and medical care?

In the last section, you read about developments in the Soviet Union and Eastern Europe following World War II. In this section, you will read about economic, political, and social changes in Western Europe, the United States, and Canada after the war. Some countries, such as Great Britain and the United States, developed welfare systems.

> **California History Social Science Standards**
>
> **10.9** Students analyze the international developments in the post-World War II world.
>
> **Focuses on:** 10.9.1

ORGANIZING YOUR THOUGHTS

Use the chart below to help you take notes. In the late 1950s, six countries in Western Europe created the European Economic Community, also known as the Common Market. Identify the six original members of the Common Market.

Common Market	
1.	2.
3.	4.
5.	6.

Reading Essentials and Study Guide

Chapter 12, Section 3 *(continued)*

- ## Western Europe: Recovery and New Unity *(page 598)*

With the help of the Marshall Plan, the countries of Western Europe recovered rapidly. By 1950, industrial output in Europe was 30 percent above prewar levels. The 1950s and 1960s were a period of dramatic growth and prosperity in Western Europe.

After the war, one man, the war hero Charles de Gaulle, dominated France. In 1946, de Gaulle helped established a new government called the Fourth Republic. It had a strong parliament and a weak presidency. No party was strong enough to dominate, and the government was largely ineffective. De Gaulle was unhappy with the Fourth Republic and withdrew from politics. In 1958, French leaders asked de Gaulle to form a new government and revise the constitution. He drafted a new constitution for the Fifth Republic that increased the power of the presidency. The president would now have the right to choose the prime minister, dissolve parliament, and supervise defense and foreign policy. French voters overwhelmingly approved the new constitution. De Gaulle became the first president of the Fifth Republic.

To achieve the status of a world power, de Gaulle invested heavily in nuclear weapons. France exploded its first nuclear bomb in 1960. During de Gaulle's presidency, the French economy grew rapidly. France became a major industrial producer and exporter, especially of automobiles and weapons. But there were still problems. Large government deficits and a rise in the cost of living led to unrest. In May 1968, a series of student protests was followed by a general labor strike. De Gaulle resigned in April 1969 and died within a year.

The three Western zones of Germany were unified as the Federal Republic of Germany in 1949. From 1949 to 1963, Konrad Adenauer was chancellor (head of state). He cooperated with the United States and other Western European nations. Under Adenauer, West Germany experienced an "economic miracle." Unemployment fell from 8 percent in 1950 to 0.4 percent in 1965. Adenauer resigned in 1963. Ludwig Erhard, who continued Adenauer's policies, succeeded him. An economic downturn in the mid-1960s opened the door to the Social Democratic Party, a moderate socialist party. It became the leading party in 1969. Willy Brandt, the mayor of West Berlin, led the Social Democrats.

Great Britain had serious economic problems at the end of World War II. In elections after the war, the Labour Party defeated Churchill's Conservative Party. The Labour Party had promised many reforms, especially in the area of social welfare. The Labour government set out to create a modern **welfare state** (a state in which the government takes responsibility for providing citizens with services and a minimal standard of living). In 1946, the new government passed the National Insurance Act and the National Health

Reading Essentials and Study Guide

Chapter 12, Section 3 *(continued)*

Service Act. The insurance act provided government funds to help the unemployed, the sick, and the aged. The health act created a system of socialized medicine that ensured medical care for everyone. The cost of building a welfare state at home forced the British to reduce expenses abroad. This meant the end of the British Empire. Britain was forced to give in to the demands of its colonies for independence. Britain was no longer able to play the <u>role</u> of a world power. Economic problems brought the Conservatives back into power from 1951 to 1964. The Conservatives favored private enterprise, but they accepted the welfare state. They even added to it by starting a building program to improve British housing.

In 1957, France, West Germany, Belgium, the Netherlands, Luxembourg, and Italy signed the Rome Treaty. This treaty created the European Economic Community (EEC), also known as the Common Market. The EEC was a free-trade area made up of the six member nations. These six nations agreed not to impose any tariffs (import charges) on each other's goods. As a group, they would be protected by a tariff on goods from non-EEC nations. All the member nations benefited economically. By the 1960s, the EEC had become an important trading **bloc** (a group of nations with a common purpose). With a total population of 165 million, the EEC was the world's largest exporter and purchaser of raw materials.

> **Academic Vocabulary**
>
> **role:** a function or part performed in a particular development or process (p. 599)

7. How did the British Empire come to an end?

_____

_____

_____

_____

• American Dominance *(page 600)*

The New Deal had brought basic changes to American society. These changes included an increase in the role and power of the federal government and the beginning of a welfare state. Other changes included the growth of organized labor and the realization of the need to deal fairly with the concerns of minorities, especially African Americans. The New Deal tradition continued when Democrats were elected president—Harry Truman in 1948, John Kennedy in 1960, and Lyndon Johnson in 1964. Even the election of a Republican president, Dwight Eisenhower, in 1952 and 1956 did not change the basic direction of the New Deal.

An economic boom followed World War II. A shortage of consumer goods during the war had left many Americans with extra income and the desire to buy goods after the war. The growth of labor unions brought higher wages and gave more workers the ability to buy consumer goods. Between 1945 and

Reading Essentials and Study Guide

Chapter 12, Section 3 (continued)

1973, **real wages** (the actual purchasing power of income) grew an average of 3 percent a year.

Cold War struggles made many Americans afraid that Communists had infiltrated the United States. The threat seemed even more real when thousands of American soldiers were sent to Korea to fight against Communist aggression. This climate of fear produced a dangerous politician, Senator Joseph McCarthy. He created a "Red Scare" (fear of communist subversion) by charging that hundreds of communists were in high government positions. Several people, including intellectuals and movie stars, were questioned about Communist activities. When McCarthy attacked alleged "Communist conspirators" in the U.S. Army, Congress condemned him in 1954. His antiCommunist crusade soon came to an end.

The 1960s began on a youthful and optimistic note. At age 43, John F. Kennedy became the youngest elected president in U.S. history. His administration was cut short when an assassin killed him on November 22, 1963. Vice President Lyndon Johnson then became president. Johnson pursued the growth of the welfare state. His programs included health care for the elderly, various programs to combat poverty, and federal assistance for education. His other passion was the **civil rights movement.** This movement had its beginnings in 1954 when the U.S. Supreme Court ruled that the practice of racial segregation (separation) in public schools was illegal. In August 1963, Martin Luther King, Jr., leader of a growing movement for racial equality, led a march on Washington, D.C. King believed in the principle of passive disobedience practiced by Mohandas Gandhi. By the end of 1963, a majority of the American people called civil rights the most significant national issue. President Johnson took up the cause of civil rights. The Civil Rights Act of 1964 began the process of ending segregation and discrimination in the workplace and all public places. The Voting Rights Act of 1965 made it easier for African Americans to vote in Southern states.

In the North and West, blacks had had voting rights for many years. But local patterns of segregation led to higher unemployment for blacks than for whites. In the summer of 1965, race riots broke out in the Watts district of Los Angeles. Thirty-four people were killed. In 1968, Martin Luther King, Jr., was assassinated. Riots broke out in over a hundred cities. The riots led to a "white backlash" (whites became less sympathetic to the cause of racial equality).

Antiwar protests also divided the American people. As the Vietnam War progressed, protests grew. In 1970, four students at Kent State University were killed by the Ohio National Guard during a student demonstration. Many Americans became less willing to continue the war. The riots and antiwar demonstrations caused many people to call for "law and order." Richard Nixon used this appeal when he was elected president in 1968. With his election, a shift to the right began in American politics.

Reading Essentials and Study Guide

Chapter 12, Section 3 *(continued)*

Canada had always had a strong export economy based on its abundant natural resources. After World War II, it developed electronic, aircraft, nuclear, and chemical engineering industries. Much of the Canadian growth was financed by capital from the United States. This led to U.S. ownership of Canadian businesses, and many Canadians worried that the United States would dominate their country economically. Canada sought to establish its own identity in world politics. It was a founding member of the United Nations and joined the North Atlantic Treaty Organization in 1949. The Liberal Party dominated Canadian politics throughout most of this period. The Liberal government created Canada's welfare state, which included a national social security system and a national health insurance program.

8. What were some of the important events in the civil rights movement from 1954 to 1965?

_____

_____

_____

_____

_____

Reading Essentials and Study Guide

Chapter 12, Section 3 *(continued)*

• Changing Values in Western Society *(page 603)*

After World War II, Western societies experienced rapid change. New inventions, such as televisions, computers, and jet planes altered the pace and nature of human life. Changes in the middle class were especially noticeable. The middle class had traditionally included businesspeople, lawyers, doctors, and teachers. A new group of managers and technicians now joined the ranks of the middle class. Changes also occurred in the lower classes. The number of farmers declined drastically. The number of industrial workers also began to decline, as the number of white-collar workers increased. An increase in the real wages of workers made it possible for them to imitate the buying patterns of the middle class. This led to what some people have called the **consumer society** (a society preoccupied with buying goods). Buying on credit became widespread in the 1950s. Workers could now buy such products as televisions, washing machines, refrigerators, vacuum cleaners, stereos, and automobiles.

Women's roles also began to change. After World War I, many governments had expressed thanks to women by granting them voting rights, including Sweden, Great Britain, Germany, Poland, Hungary, Austria, Czechoslovakia and the United States. Women in France gained the right to vote in 1944, while Italian women gained this right in 1945. During World War II, women had entered the workforce in huge numbers. At the end of the war, many of them were let go to provide jobs for soldiers returning home. For a time, many women fell back into traditional roles. Birthrates rose, creating a "baby boom" in the late 1940s and the 1950s.

By the end of the 1950s, the birthrate began to fall, and the size of families decreased. The number of married women in the workforce increased in both Europe and the United States. These women faced an old problem. They still earned less than men for equal work. Women also tended to enter traditionally female jobs. Many faced the burden of earning income and raising a family at the same time. These inequalities led many women to rebel. In the late 1960s, there was a renewed interest in feminism, or the **women's liberation movement,** as it was now called. Simone de Beauvoir <u>published</u> *The Second Sex* which influenced the women's movements in both Europe and the United States.

Academic Vocabulary
publish: to make the work of an author public in the form of a book or novel (p. 604)

Before World War II, most of the people who went to universities were from the wealthier classes. After the war, European countries began to encourage more people to get a higher education by eliminating fees. Enrollments grew dramatically as students from the middle and lower classes began to attend. There were problems, however. Many European university classrooms were overcrowded. Many professors paid little attention to their students.

Reading Essentials and Study Guide

Chapter 12, Section 3 *(continued)*

Growing discontent led to student protests in the late 1960s. Many of these protests were an extension of the revolts in U.S. universities. Some students wanted to reform the university system. They did not believe that universities responded to their needs or to the realities of the modern world. Student protest movements in both Europe and the United States reached a high point in 1968. By the early 1970s, however, the movements had largely disappeared.

9. How did women's roles change during and after World War II?

_____

_____

_____

_____

_____

Reading Essentials and Study Guide

Chapter 13, Section 1

For use with textbook pages 615–619

DECLINE OF THE SOVIET UNION

CONTENT VOCABULARY

détente a relaxation of tensions and improved relations between two adversaries, especially used for American-Soviet relations in the 1970s *(page 616)*

dissident a person who speaks out against the regime in power *(page 616)*

perestroika ("restructuring") Mikhail Gorbachev's plan for economic reforms in the Soviet Union in the late 1980s *(page 617)*

DRAWING FROM EXPERIENCE

Have you heard of the "evil empire"? Who used this expression? What country was he talking about?

In this section, you will learn about changes in the Soviet Union in the 1980s and 1990s.

California History Social Science Standards
10.9 Students analyze the international developments in the post-World War II world.
Focuses on: 10.9.7

ORGANIZING YOUR THOUGHTS

Use the chart below to help you take notes. Identify the rulers of the Soviet Union, and later the Russian Republic, following Nikita Khrushchev.

| Nikita Khrushchev | → | 1. | → | 2. | → |

| 3. | → | 4. | |

Reading Essentials and Study Guide

Chapter 13, Section 1 *(continued)*

READ TO LEARN

• The Soviet System Under Stress *(page 616)*

When Nikita Khrushchev was removed from office in 1964, two men, Alexei Kosygin and Leonid Brezhnev, replaced him. Brezhnev became the dominant leader. He was determined to keep Eastern Europe in Communist hands and was not interested in reform. He insisted on the right of the Soviet Union to intervene if communism was threatened in another Communist state. This was known as the Brezhnev Doctrine. Under Brezhnev, the government did allow more access to Western styles of music, dress, and art. But **dissidents** (those who spoke out against the regime) were still punished.

Brezhnev continued to emphasize heavy industry. Problems weakened the Soviet economy. The government's central planning led to a huge, complex bureaucracy. This discouraged efficiency and led to indifference. Collective farmers also had no incentive to work hard. Communist party leaders and leaders of the army and secret police enjoyed a high standard of living and had become corrupt.

In the 1970s, relations between the United States and the Soviet Union improved. This phase in U.S.-Soviet relations is called **détente** (the relaxation of tensions between nations). The United States began to sell grain and consumer goods to the Soviet Union. The <u>apparent</u> collapse of détente began with the Soviet invasion of Afghanistan in 1979. The Soviet Union wanted to restore a pro-Soviet regime there, which the United States viewed as an act of <u>expansion</u>. President Jimmy Carter stopped the shipment of grain to the Soviet Union. He also would not allow Americans to participate in the 1980 Olympic Games, which were held in Moscow.

Academic Vocabulary
apparent: open to view; obvious (p. 616)

Academic Vocabulary
expansion: the act or process of expanding or gaining land (p. 616)

The Cold War intensified when Ronald Reagan was elected president in 1980. Reagan called the Soviet Union an "evil empire" and began a new arms race. Reagan also gave military aid to rebels fighting a pro-Soviet regime in Afghanistan. By 1980, the Soviet Union was in serious trouble, with a declining economy, a rise in infant mortality rates and alcoholism, and poor working conditions. Within the Communist Party, a small group of reformers emerged.

5. What problems in the Soviet Union led to reform?

_____

_____

_____

_____

_____

Reading Essentials and Study Guide

Chapter 13, Section 1 *(continued)*

• Gorbachev and Soviet Reform *(page 617)*

When Mikhail Gorbachev became the leader of the Soviet Union in 1985, changes began that eventually ended the Cold War. Gorbachev made an agreement with the United States in 1987 to eliminate intermediate-range nuclear weapons. Both sides had reasons to slow down the arms race. Gorbachev hoped to make economic and other reforms in the Soviet Union. The national debt in the United States had tripled, and the United States had moved from being a creditor nation (a nation that exports more than it imports) to being the world's biggest debtor nation. By 1990, both countries knew that their large military budgets would make it difficult to solve their domestic problems.

Gorbachev stopped giving military support to Communist governments in Eastern Europe. This opened the door to the overthrow of Communist governments in these countries. A revolutionary movement swept through Eastern Europe in 1989. Germany was reunified on October 3, 1990. In 1991, the Soviet Union was dissolved. The Cold War had come to an end.

From the start, Gorbachev saw the need for radical reforms. The basis of these reforms was **perestroika** (restructuring). At first, this meant restructuring economic policy. Gorbachev wanted to start a market economy, in which consumers influence what is produced. But Gorbachev soon realized that it was not possible to reform the economy without political reform. In 1988, Gorbachev established a new Soviet parliament, the Congress of People's Deputies. The members were elected and met in 1989. In 1990, Gorbachev allowed non-Communist political parties to organize. At the same time, he strengthened his own power by creating a new position—president of the Soviet Union. In March 1990, Gorbachev became the Soviet Union's first (and last) president.

As Gorbachev loosened the control of the Communist Party, ethnic tensions in the Soviet Union surfaced. Nationalist movements emerged throughout the republics of the Soviet Union. In 1989 and 1990, there were calls for independence in Soviet Georgia, Latvia, Estonia, Moldavia, Uzbekistan, Azerbaijan, and Lithuania. By 1991, many Soviet leaders were worried. The breakup of the Soviet Union would mean an end to their privileges. On August 19, 1991, a group of conservative leaders arrested Gorbachev and tried to seize power. The attempt failed. Boris Yeltsin, president of the Russian Republic, and thousands of Russians resisted the takeover. The Soviet republics now moved for complete independence. Ukraine voted for independence on December 1, 1991. A week later, the leaders of Russia, Ukraine, and Belarus announced that the Soviet Union had "ceased to exist." Gorbachev resigned on December 25, 1991, and turned his responsibilities over to Boris Yeltsin, the new president of Russia.

Reading Essentials and Study Guide

Chapter 13, Section 1 (continued)

Boris Yeltsin was committed to introducing a free market economy as quickly as possible, but the transition was not easy. Economic hardships were made worse by a rise in organized crime. Yeltsin also used force against Chechnya, who wanted to secede from Russia and create their own republic. At the end of 1999, Yeltsin resigned and was replaced by Vladimir Putin. Putin vowed to return the breakaway state of Chechnya to Russian authority. In September 2004, more than 300 died when Russian troops attempted to free a school seized by Chechnyan rebels.

In July 2001, Putin began reforms to strengthen the Russian economy. The reforms included the free purchase and sale of land and tax cuts. Since then, Russia had experienced a growing economy.

6. What series of events led to the end of the Soviet Union?

_____

_____

_____

_____

_____

Reading Essentials and Study Guide

Chapter 13, Section 2

For use with textbook pages 620–624

EASTERN EUROPE

CONTENT VOCABULARY
ethnic cleansing the policy of killing or forcibly removing an ethnic group from its lands; used by the Serbs in Bosnia *(page 623)*
autonomous self-governing *(page 623)*

DRAWING FROM EXPERIENCE

Have you ever seen pictures of the Berlin Wall? What did it look like? Why was it built? Why did it fall?

In the last section, you read about the fall of communism in the Soviet Union. In this section, you will read about the fall of communism in other countries in Eastern Europe.

ORGANIZING YOUR THOUGHTS

Use the chart below to help you take notes. Describe how communism ended in the countries in this chart. Also indicate some results of the revolutions in these countries.

California History Social Science Standards

10.9 Students analyze the international developments in the post-World War II world.
10.10 Students analyze instances of nation-building in the contemporary world in two of the following regions or countries: the Middle East, Africa, Mexico, and other parts of Latin America, and China.

Focuses on:
10.9.5, 10.9.7, 10.10.1, 10.10.2, 10.10.3

Country	How Communism Ended	Results of Revolution
Poland	1.	2.
Czechoslovakia	3.	4.
Romania	5.	6.
East Germany	7.	8.
Yugoslavia	9.	10.

Reading Essentials and Study Guide

Chapter 13, Section 2 (continued)

READ TO LEARN

• Revolutions in Eastern Europe (page 621)

People in Eastern Europe had not always been happy with their Soviet-style Communist governments. After Gorbachev made it clear that the Soviet Union would not intervene militarily in their countries, revolutions broke out throughout Eastern Europe.

In Poland, workers' protests led to changes. In 1980, a worker named Lech Walesa organized a national trade union known as Solidarity. Solidarity gained the support of the workers and the Roman Catholic Church. During a period of military rule in the 1980s, Walesa was arrested, but the movement continued. After more demonstrations in 1988, the Polish government agreed to free parliamentary elections—the first in Eastern Europe in 40 years. A new government was elected, ending 45 years of Communist rule. In December 1990, Walesa was chosen as president. But the new path was not easy. Free-market reforms led to severe unemployment and discontent. At the end of 1995, a former Communist defeated Walesa and became the new president. However, he continued Poland's move toward a prosperous free-market economy.

In Czechoslovakia, mass demonstrations took place in 1988 and 1989. In December 1989, the Communist government collapsed. At the end of December, Václav Havel became the new president. He was a writer who had played an important role in bringing down the Communist government. The new government in Czechoslovakia faced old ethnic conflicts. The two national groups, Czechs and Slovaks, agreed to a peaceful division of the country. On January 1, 1993, Czechoslovakia split into the Czech Republic and Slovakia.

In Romania, the Communist leader Nicolae Ceauşescu had set up a rigid dictatorship in 1965. He used secret police to crush all dissent. His economic policies led to a sharp drop in living standards, including food shortages and the rationing of bread, flour, and sugar. His plan for rapid urbanization also made the Romanian people angry. Entire villages were bulldozed as part of the plan. In December 1989, the secret police murdered thousands of people who were peacefully demonstrating. Finally, the army refused to support any more repression. Ceauşescu and his wife were captured and executed. A new government was quickly formed.

In East Germany, Erich Honecker became head of the Communist Party in 1971. He used the Stasi, the secret police, to rule for the next 18 years. In 1989, many East Germans began to flee their country. Mass demonstrations broke out in the fall of 1989. On November 9, the Communist government gave in and opened its border with the West. Thousands of East Germans rushed across the border. Families who had not seen each other in years were reunited. People on both sides of the Berlin Wall began tearing the wall down. The government gave in again and ordered the rest of the wall torn down.

Reading Essentials and Study Guide

Chapter 13, Section 2 *(continued)*

During East Germany's first free elections in March 1990, the Christian Democrats won almost 50 percent of the vote. The Christian Democrats supported reunification with West Germany. The reunification of Germany took place on October 3, 1990.

11. What series of events led to the reunification of Germany?

_____

_____

_____

_____

_____

• The Disintegration of Yugoslavia *(page 623)*

Although Yugoslavia had a Communist government, it had never been a Soviet satellite state. After Tito died in 1980, a government composed of representatives from the six republics and two provinces of Yugoslavia kept the country under Communist rule. By 1990, new parties had emerged, and the Communist Party lost its power.

The situation in Yugoslavia was complex. In 1990, the Yugoslav republics of Slovenia, Croatia, Bosnia-Herzegovina, and Macedonia began to push for independence. Slobodan Milošević, who became the leader of Serbia in 1987, was against their plans, because the republics included Serb minorities. He wanted to redraw borders to include the Serb minorities in a new Greater Serbian state. In June 1991, Slovenia and Croatia declared their independence. In September, the Yugoslavian army began a full assault against Croatia. Serbia dominated the Yugoslavian army. Before a cease-fire was arranged, the Serbian forces captured one-third of Croatia's territory.

In 1992, the Serbs began an assault against Bosnia-Herzegovina. By mid-1993, Serbian forces had acquired 70 percent of Bosnian territory. Many Bosnians were Muslims. Toward them, the Serbs followed a policy they called **ethnic cleansing** (killing them or forcibly removing them from their lands). By 1995, 250,000 Bosnians (mostly civilians) had been killed, and two million others were homeless. In 1995, Bosnian and Croatian forces regained much of the territory that had been lost to Serbian forces. Air strikes by NATO bombers were launched in retaliation for Serb attacks on civilians. These attacks forced the Serbs to sign a peace treaty on December 14. The agreement split Bosnia into a loose union of a Serb republic and a Muslim-Croat federation. NATO sent a force of sixty thousand troops to monitor the area.

Reading Essentials and Study Guide

Chapter 13, Section 2 *(continued)*

Peace in Bosnia did not bring peace to the region. A new war began in 1998 over Kosovo. In 1974, Tito had made Kosovo an **autonomous** (self-governing) province within Yugoslavia. Kosovo's inhabitants were mainly ethnic Albanians. In 1989, Milošević took Kosovo's autonomous status away. Groups of ethnic Albanians <u>founded</u> the Kosovo Liberation Army in the mid-1990s and began a campaign against Serbian rule. In response, Serb forces began to massacre ethnic Albanians. The United States and NATO sought to arrange a <u>settlement</u>. In 1999, Albanians in Kosovo gained autonomy within Serbia. When Milošević objected, a NATO bombing campaign forced Yugoslav <u>cooperation</u>. Elections held in 2000 ended Milošević's rule, and he was brought to trial for his role in the bloodshed in the Balkans. In 2002, Serbia and Montenegro formed a republic. In 2003, they agreed to vote on full independence in 2006.

12. Why did Serbia oppose the other republics' plans for independence?

_____

_____

_____

_____

_____

Academic Vocabulary
founded: to establish an institution often with terms of future maintenance (p. 624)

Academic Vocabulary
settlement: an agreement resolving differences (p. 624)

Academic Vocabulary
cooperation: the act of working with others; acting together (p. 624)

Reading Essentials and Study Guide

Chapter 13, Section 3

For use with textbook pages 625–630

EUROPE AND THE UNITED STATES

CONTENT VOCABULARY

Thatcherism the economic policy of British Prime Minister Margaret Thatcher, which limited social welfare and restricted union power *(page 628)*

budget deficit spending by a government that exceeds revenues *(page 629)*

weapons of mass destruction nuclear, chemical, and biological weapons that can kill tens of thousands of people at once *(page 630)*

DRAWING FROM EXPERIENCE

Do you or your family have a budget? What kinds of things do you include in your budget? What happens if you spend more than your budget had allowed?

In the last two sections, you read about changes in the Soviet Union and Eastern Europe after 1970. In this section, you will read about developments in Western Europe and North America during this time. Economic issues dominated politics during much of this period.

ORGANIZING YOUR THOUGHTS

Use the chart below to help you take notes. Indicate the effect of economic issues on politics in the countries in this chart.

California History Social Science Standards

10.10 Students analyze instances of nation-building in the contemporary world in two of the following regions or countries: the Middle East, Africa, Mexico, and other parts of Latin America, and China. **10.11** Students analyze the integration of countries into the world economy and the information, technological, and communications revolutions (e.g., television, satellites, computers).

Effect of Economic Issues on Politics	
France	1.
Germany	2.
Great Britain	3.
United States	4.

Reading Essentials and Study Guide

Chapter 13, Section 3 *(continued)*

READ TO LEARN

• Winds of Change in Western Europe *(page 626)*

Between the early 1950s and late 1970s, Western Europe had nearly full employment. However, an economic downturn occurred in the mid-1970s and early 1980s. Inflation and unemployment rose dramatically. A dramatic increase in the price of oil after the Arab-Israeli conflict in 1973 was a major cause of the downturn. Western European economies recovered in the 1980s, but there were still problems.

The Western European nations moved toward a greater union of their economies after 1970. The European Economic Community (EEC) expanded in 1973 to include Great Britain, Ireland, and Denmark. By 1986, Spain, Portugal, and Greece had become members. Austria, Finland, and Sweden joined in 1995. The Treaty on European Union in 1994 turned the EEC into the principal organization of the new European Union (EU). One of the European Union's first goals was to establish a common European <u>currency</u>, the euro. Most of the EU nations gave up their currency in favor of the euro by January 1, 2002.

Academic Vocabulary
currency: paper money in circulation (p. 626)

France's economic problems in the 1970s caused a shift to the left politically. By 1981, the Socialists had become the chief party in the National Assembly. The Socialist leader, François Mitterrand, was elected president. To help workers, Mitterrand implemented a higher minimum wage, a 39-hour workweek, and higher taxes for the rich. The Socialist government also nationalized (took over) major banks, the steel industry, the space and electronics industries, and insurance firms. But most Socialist policies failed to work. In 1993, French unemployment was 10.6 percent. In the elections in March 1993, a coalition of conservative parties won 80 percent of the seats in the National Assembly. In 1995, conservative Jacques Chirac was elected president.

In West Germany, the Social Democrats, a moderate Socialist party, replaced the Christian Democrats as the leading party in 1969. The first Social Democratic chancellor was Willy Brandt. In December 1972, Brandt signed a treaty with East Germany that led to more cultural, personal, and economic contacts between West and East Germany. In 1982, the Christian Democratic Union of Helmut Kohl formed a new, more conservative government. When Germany was reunified in 1990, Kohl was the leader of Europe's most powerful nation.

It soon became clear that rebuilding eastern Germany would take far more money than had originally been thought. Kohl's government was forced to raise taxes. The collapse of the economy in eastern Germany led to high levels of unemployment and discontent. One result was a return to power for the Social Democrats in 1998. Unemployment and economic problems caused tensions to grow between Germans and immigrant groups. Attacks against foreigners by right-wing extremists, especially young neo-Nazis, became part of German life.

Reading Essentials and Study Guide

Chapter 13, Section 3 *(continued)*

Between 1964 and 1979, Great Britain's Conservative Party and Labour Party alternated in power. One problem both parties had to face was intense fighting between Catholics and Protestants in Northern Ireland. There were also economic problems and frequent labor strikes. In 1979, the Conservatives came to power under Margaret Thatcher. Thatcher pledged to limit social welfare, restrict union power, and end inflation. Although she did not eliminate the basic parts of the welfare system, she did break the power of the unions and controlled inflation. **Thatcherism,** as her economic policy was called, improved the British economic situation overall. The south of England, for example, prospered. But old industrial areas in other parts of the country had high unemployment and poverty. In 1990, Thatcher's government tried to replace local property taxes with a flat-rate tax for all adults. Antitax riots broke out. Thatcher's popularity fell to an all-time low, and she resigned as prime minister. The Conservative Party was now led by John Major. In the elections of 1997, the Labour Party won a landslide victory. Tony Blair, a moderate, became prime minister.

5. What were some of the problems faced by Germany after reunification?

_____

_____

_____

_____

_____

• The U.S. Domestic Scene *(page 628)*

With the election of Richard Nixon in 1968, politics in the United States shifted to the right. In his campaign for the presidency, Nixon used "law and order" issues and a slowdown in racial desegregation to appeal to Southern whites. The South, which had been a stronghold for the Democrats, began to form a new allegiance to the Republican Party. As president, Nixon used illegal <u>methods</u> to gain political information about his opponents. This led to the Watergate scandal. A group of men working for Nixon's reelection campaign broke into the Democratic national headquarters in the Watergate Hotel in Washington, D.C. They were caught trying to install electronic listening devices. At first, Nixon lied about his involvement in the affair, but secret tapes of his own conversations in the White House revealed the truth. On August 9, 1974, Nixon resigned to avoid impeachment.

Academic Vocabulary
method: a way, technique, or process of or for doing something (p. 628)

Vice President Gerald Ford became president when Nixon resigned. In the 1976 election, he lost to the former governor of Georgia, Jimmy Carter. By 1980, the Carter administration faced two serious problems. First, high rates of inflation and a decline in average weekly earnings were causing a drop in

Reading Essentials and Study Guide

Chapter 13, Section 3 *(continued)*

American living standards. Second, 52 Americans were taken hostage by the Iranian government of the Ayatollah Khomeini. Carter was unable to gain the release of the hostages. The economic problems and the hostage situation contributed to Carter's loss to Ronald Reagan in the election of 1980.

The Reagan Revolution, as it has been called, sent U.S. policy in new directions. Reagan cut back on the welfare state by decreasing spending on food stamps, school lunch programs, and job programs. At the same time, he oversaw the largest peacetime military buildup in U.S. history. The spending policies of the Reagan administration produced record budget deficits. A **budget deficit** exists when a government spends more than it collects in revenues. George Bush, Reagan's vice president, succeeded him as president.

Economic problems enabled a Democrat, Bill Clinton, to defeat Bush in the presidential election in 1992. Clinton claimed to be a new kind of Democrat—one who favored a number of the Republican policies of the 1980s. An economic revival helped Clinton to be reelected. However, much of his second term was overshadowed by charges of misconduct. The House of Representatives voted two articles of impeachment (formal charges of misconduct) against him. He was tried in the Senate and acquitted. Clinton's problems helped the Republican candidate, George W. Bush, win a very close presidential election in 2000. President Bush directed much of his attention to fighting terrorism, stimulating the economy, and lowering unemployment.

The terrorist attacks of September 11, 2001 led to the war on terrorism. The United States entered armed conflict in Afghanistan, a training ground for terrorists. Then, the United States invaded Iraq based on statements that the dictator Saddam Hussein possessed **weapons of mass destruction.** President Bush was elected for a second term in 2004 after a bitterly fought campaign with a record turnout. Some analysts concluded that Americans chose to reelect the leader who had proclaimed the war on terrorism.

6. Why did President Nixon resign?

_____

_____

_____

_____

Reading Essentials and Study Guide

Chapter 13, Section 4

For use with textbook pages 631–639

WESTERN SOCIETY AND CULTURE

CONTENT VOCABULARY

globalization a term with both positive and negative connotations referring to the trend toward development of a global economy and culture *(page 632)*

gender parity policies that encourage more women to become part of government *(page 634)*

cultural imperialism the idea that a Western nation controls other world cultures, much as they had actual governments of colonies in the age of imperialism *(page 636)*

DRAWING FROM EXPERIENCE

Where were you when you heard about the attacks on the World Trade Center Towers? How did this event affect your life?

In the last section, you read about economic and political developments in Western Europe and North America in the late twentieth century. In this section, you will read about changes in Western society and culture during this time. The growth of terrorism has had a great impact on Western countries.

ORGANIZING YOUR THOUGHTS

Use the diagram below to help you take notes. American culture has increasingly influenced other parts of the world since the end of World War II. Indicate four ways that American culture has influenced other countries.

> **California History Social Science Standards**
>
> **10.10** Students analyze instances of nation-building in the contemporary world in two of the following regions or countries: the Middle East, Africa, Mexico, and other parts of Latin America, and China.
> **10.11** Students analyze the integration of countries into the world economy and the information, technological, and communications revolutions (e.g., television, satellites, computers).
> **Focuses on:**
> 10.10.2

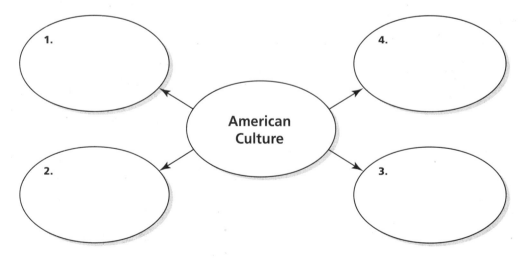

Reading Essentials and Study Guide

Chapter 13, Section 4 *(continued)*

READ TO LEARN

- ## The Quickening Pace of Change *(page 632)*

Since 1970, the pace of change has quickened and promoted **globalization**. Scientific and technological achievements since World War II have revolutionized people's lives. By sponsoring projects, governments created a new model for scientific research on complex projects that required large teams of scientists and sophisticated laboratories. In the 1960s and 1970s, people began to worry that technological advances were having side effects that were damaging to the environment. People continue to disagree over the proper role of science.

In October 1999, the world population reached 6 billion people. It is expected to reach 9.3 billion by 2050. In wealthy regions, population is declining and "graying"—a larger <u>percentage</u> of the population is reaching retirement. An older population places a demand on the economy because the taxes of the workers must be stretched further to cover the expenses of the elderly.

> **Academic Vocabulary**
>
> **percentage:** a part of a whole expressed in hundredths obtained by multiplying a number by a percent (p. 633)

Trends in marriage and divorce have changed as well. The number of people in Europe getting married has decreased and people tend to marry at a slightly older age. In addition, the divorce rate has increased. These trends have meant a lower birthrate, and thus an older population overall. Women's changing roles have affected family size as well.

Since 1970, more and more women have entered the workforce in Western countries. In the 1960s and 1970s, the women's movement emerged. Women remain underrepresented in most national legislatures. Some European countries have adopted **gender parity**, policies that encourage more women to become part of government, by requiring that women make up either a certain number of candidates or a certain number of those elected.

AIDS, an incurable disease that attacks the immune system, was discovered in 1981. This disease was especially frightening during the first few years after its discovery because no one knew exactly how it was transmitted. This led to discrimination against people with AIDS, even after scientists proved that the disease was not transmitted through casual contact. During the late 1980s and 1990s, public education campaigns helped promote awareness. However, AIDS remains a serious global issue.

5. What is "gender parity"?

_____

_____

_____

_____

Reading Essentials and Study Guide

Chapter 13, Section 4 *(continued)*

- ## Popular Culture and National Identity *(page 635)*

With new technology, culture can be mass-produced and marketed globally. Popular culture is entertainment for a mass audience to make a profit. Ever since the 1920s, popular culture has become more important. By the 1990s, popular culture was becoming similar the world over.

Some countries worried that American entertainment was weakening their own language and culture. This has been called **cultural imperialism,** meaning that a Western nation controlled other world cultures, much as they had controlled governments in the 1800s. There are trends in the other direction, though. Reggae music, world music programming on public radio stations, and Latin pop have all become popular.

In the postwar years, sports became big business. Through television, sports were transformed into a worldwide experience. Many sports organizations began to receive most of their revenues from television contracts.

Sports have become big politics as well as big business. Unfortunately, this has sometimes led to violence. An example of the mix of politics and sports is the Olympic Games. The United States boycotted the 1980 Moscow Olympics and the Soviets responded by refusing to participate in the Los Angeles Games in 1984. Sports can also be a positive political force. In 1998, when the French soccer team defeated Brazil, the celebrations were larger than any since France's <u>liberation</u> in World War II.

Academic Vocabulary
liberation: the act of freeing a country from domination by a foreign power (p. 637)

Christianity has dominated the spiritual life of Western society since the Middle Ages. After World War II, however, immigration brought greater religious diversity to Europe. It is possible that religion serves as a way to strengthen a sense of community in an increasingly complex society. Religion has also become a powerful political force in America. Controversies have erupted over to what extent religion and government should be separated.

It is a challenge to maintain national and regional identities in a global culture. Ethnic, religious, and minority groups use different tactics to reach their goals. Most movements are peaceful. However, some minorities use violence to win concessions.

6. What is "cultural imperialism"?

_____

_____

_____

_____

Reading Essentials and Study Guide

Chapter 14, Section 1

For use with textbook pages 649–655

GENERAL TRENDS IN LATIN AMERICA

CONTENT VOCABULARY

multinational corporation a company with divisions in more than two countries *(page 651)*

megacities cities with rapidly increasing populations, having trouble keeping up with urban services *(page 654)*

favelas squatter settlements lacking basic urban services *(page 654)*

magic realism a form of expression unique to Latin American literature; it combines realistic events with dreamlike or fantastic backgrounds *(page 654)*

DRAWING FROM EXPERIENCE

Have you ever bought anything that was grown or made in a Latin American country? If so, what?

In this section, you will learn about developments in Latin America since the end of World War II. Exporting raw materials and importing manufactured goods led to economic and political problems for many Latin American nations.

ORGANIZING YOUR THOUGHTS

Use the chart below to help you take notes. For each topic in the chart, describe its effect on the countries of Latin America.

> **California History Social Science Standards**
>
> **10.9** Students analyze the international developments in the post-World War II world.
> **10.10** Students analyze instances of nation-building in the contemporary world in two of the following regions or countries: the Middle East, Africa, Mexico, and other parts of Latin America, and China.
>
> **Focuses on:**
> 10.9.1, 10.10.2, 10.10.3

Effect on Latin American Countries of:	
the Great Depression	**1.**
multinational corporations	**2.**
borrowing from foreign countries	**3.**
debt crisis	**4.**
population growth	**5.**
the Cold War	**6.**

Reading Essentials and Study Guide

Chapter 14, Section 1 (continued)

READ TO LEARN

- **Economic and Political Developments** (page 650)

Since colonial times, Latin Americans had exported raw materials and imported manufactured goods from industrialized countries. As a result of the Great Depression, exports declined, and the Latin American countries did not have the money they needed to buy imported goods. In response, many Latin American countries developed their own industries to produce goods that had been imported previously.

The United States has always played a large role in Latin America. For years, the United States sent troops into Latin American countries to protect U.S. interests and to help dictators that were friendly to the United States. In 1948, the countries of the Western Hemisphere formed the Organization of American States (OAS). The OAS called for an end to military involvement by one state in the affairs of any other state. But the formation of the OAS did not end U.S. involvement in Latin American affairs. As the Cold War developed, the United States took action when it believed that Soviet agents were trying to establish Communist governments. The United States also provided huge amounts of military aid to anti-Communist governments.

In the 1960s, military governments in Chile, Brazil, and Argentina returned to export-import economies <u>financed</u> by foreigners. These governments also encouraged **multinational corporations** (companies with divisions in more than two countries) to come to Latin America. Multinational corporations made these countries more dependent on industrialized nations. In the 1970s, Latin American nations became even more dependent as they tried to maintain their weak economies by borrowing money. By 1982, many Latin American economies had begun to crumble. Wages fell. Unemployment and inflation skyrocketed. To get new loans, Latin American governments were now forced to make basic reforms. During this process, many people began to believe that government had taken control of too many industries.

Academic Vocabulary
finance: to provide with necessary funds (p. 651)

With the debt crisis of the 1980s came a movement toward democracy. Some military leaders were unwilling to deal with the huge debt problems. Many people also began to realize that military power alone could not create a strong state. By the mid-1990s, several democratic governments had been created. One serious effect of poverty is the drug trade. Starving peasants grow coca and opium, which they sell to drug lords who supply the world with cocaine and heroin. The revival of democracy was sometimes fragile. For example, in 1992, President Fujimori of Peru returned that country to an authoritarian system.

7. What is a multinational corporation?

_____

_____

_____

Reading Essentials and Study Guide

Chapter 14, Section 1 *(continued)*

• **Latin American Society** *(page 653)*

Latin America's economic problems were made worse by dramatic growth in population. By the mid-1980s, the population of Latin America had grown to 400 million. With the increase in population, there was an increase in the size of cities. By 2000, 50 Latin American cities had over a million people. Slums or shantytowns became part of many of these cities. Some cities have become extremely large. In 2004 an estimated 17 million people lived in Sao Paulo, and 18 million lived in Mexico City. Cities such as these are called **megacities,** cities that have grown so fast that regular city services (housing, plumbing, water supply, and schools) cannot be provided. Many people live in **favelas,** squatter settlements where clean water and electricity are rare. There continues to be a wide gap between rich and poor in Latin American societies. The role of women in Latin America has changed. Although the traditional roles of wife and mother are highly respected, many women have moved into new jobs in industry, law, and medicine.

8. What is a megacity?

_____

_____

_____

_____

_____

Reading Essentials and Study Guide

Chapter 14, Section 1 *(continued)*

• **Latin American Culture** *(page 654)*

Writers and artists in Latin America have a very high status. They are seen as people who can express the hopes of the people. In literature, Latin Americans developed a unique form of expression called **magic realism.** Magic realism brings together realistic events with dreamlike or fantastic backgrounds. Perhaps the best example of magic realism is *One Hundred Years of Solitude,* a novel by Gabriel García Márquez. Márquez was awarded the Nobel Prize for literature.

Latin American art and architecture were strongly influenced by international <u>trends</u> after World War II. In painting, abstract styles were especially important. Some of the best examples of modern architecture can be seen in Brasília, the capital city of Brazil. Latin America's greatest modern architect, Oscar Niemeyer, designed some of the major buildings in Brasília.

Academic Vocabulary
trend: current style or preference (p. 654)

9. Why do writers and artists enjoy a high status in Latin America?

_____

_____

_____

_____

_____

Reading Essentials and Study Guide

Chapter 14, Section 2

For use with textbook pages 658–662

MEXICO, CUBA, AND CENTRAL AMERICA

CONTENT VOCABULARY

PRI Institutional Revolutionary Party *(page 659)*

privatization the sale of government-owned companies to private firms *(page 660)*

trade embargo a policy prohibiting trade with a particular country *(page 660)*

contras rebels financed by the United States who began a guerrilla war against the Sandinista government in Nicaragua *(page 662)*

DRAWING FROM EXPERIENCE

How far is Cuba from the United States? What kind of relationship does our country have with Cuba? Have you ever bought any goods grown or made in Cuba? Why do you think this is so?

In the last section, you read about general trends in all of Latin America. In this section, you will read about economic and political crises in Mexico, Cuba, and Central America following World War II.

ORGANIZING YOUR THOUGHTS

Use the chart below to help you take notes. The United States has been involved in the affairs of many Latin American countries. Describe U.S. relations after World War II with the countries in this chart.

> **California History Social Science Standards**
>
> **10.9** Students analyze the international developments in the post-World War II world. **10.10** Students analyze instances of nation-building in the contemporary world in two of the following regions or countries: the Middle East, Africa, Mexico, and other parts of Latin America, and China.
>
> **Focuses on:**
> 10.9.1, 10.10.2, 10.10.3

U.S. Relations With:	
Cuba	1.
El Salvador	2.
Nicaragua	3.
Panama	4.

Copyright © by The McGraw-Hill Companies, Inc.

Reading Essentials and Study Guide

Chapter 14, Section 2 *(continued)*

READ TO LEARN

- ## The Mexican Way *(page 659)*

The official political party of the Mexican Revolution was the Institutional Revolutionary Party **(PRI).** It came to dominate Mexico. Every six years, leaders of the PRI chose the party's presidential candidate, who was then elected by the people. During the 1950s and 1960s, economic growth led to real gains in wages for more and more people in Mexico. At the end of the 1960s, however, students began to <u>challenge</u> the one-party system in Mexico. On October 2, 1968, university students gathered in Mexico City to protest government policies. Police forces opened fire and killed hundreds. People became concerned about the need for change. The next two presidents, Luís Echeverría and José López Portillo, made political reforms and opened the door to new political parties. Greater freedom of debate in the press and universities was allowed.

In the late 1970s, new reserves of oil were discovered in Mexico. The sale of oil abroad increased dramatically. The government became more dependent on oil revenues. When oil prices dropped in the mid-1980s, Mexico was no longer able to make payments on its foreign debt. The government was forced to adopt new economic policies. One <u>element</u> of these policies was **privatization** (the sale of government-owned companies to private firms). The debt crisis and rising unemployment caused support for the PRI to drop. In 2000, Vicente Fox defeated the PRI candidate for the presidency. One of Fox's top priorities was finding a solution to the immigration problem. He met with U.S. president George W. Bush, and in 2004 Bush backed a program to give temporary visas to illegal workers. Fox proposed a grant of amnesty to illegal Mexican workers in the United States. However, many Americans believe these reforms would take jobs away from American workers.

> **Academic Vocabulary**
>
> **challenge:** to dispute as being unjust, invalid, or outdated (p. 659)

> **Academic Vocabulary**
>
> **element:** one of a number of distinct groups composing a larger group (p. 660)

5. What was the effect of the discovery of oil on the Mexican economy?

_____

_____

_____

_____

_____

- ## The Cuban Revolution *(page 660)*

In the 1950s, a strong opposition movement arose in Cuba. The movement was led by Fidel Castro and overthrew the government of the dictator Fulgencio Batista in 1959. Many Cubans who disagreed with Castro fled to the United States. When Cuba began to receive aid and arms from the Soviet Union and Eastern Europe, relations with the United States deteriorated. In October 1960, the United States declared a **trade embargo** (prohibited trade)

Reading Essentials and Study Guide

Chapter 14, Section 2 *(continued)*

and broke all diplomatic relations with Cuba. In April 1961, the American president, John F. Kennedy, supported an attempt to overthrow Castro's government. When the invasion at the Bay of Pigs failed, the Soviets decided to make an even greater commitment to Cuba. In December 1961, Castro declared that he was a Marxist. The Soviets began placing missiles in Cuba in 1962, which led to the Cuban missile crisis.

The Cuban missile crisis caused Castro to realize that the Soviet Union had been unreliable. Castro tried to start his own revolutionary movement in the rest of Latin America, but this failed. Castro's Marxist government continued in Cuba, but with mixed results. The Cuban people did benefit in some ways. The government provided free medical services for all citizens. Illiteracy in Cuba was nearly eliminated.

The Cuban economy relied on the production and sale of sugar. Economic problems forced Castro's government to depend on Soviet aid and the purchase of Cuban sugar by Soviet bloc countries. After the collapse of these Communist governments in 1989, Cuba lost their support. Economic conditions in Cuba have steadily declined, but Castro has managed to remain in power.

6. How did the collapse of Communist governments in Eastern Europe affect Cuba?

_____

_____

_____

_____

_____

• Upheaval in Central America *(page 661)*

Central America includes seven countries: Costa Rica, Nicaragua, Honduras, El Salvador, Panama, Belize and Guatemala. Central America has depended on the export of bananas, coffee, and cotton. Prices for these products have varied over time. This has created economic crises at different times. A huge gulf between the wealthy elite and poor peasants in these countries has also created a climate of instability. Fear of communism has often led the United States to support repressive regimes in this area.

In El Salvador, the wealthy elite and the military controlled the government after World War II. In the late 1970s and the 1980s, El Salvador was torn apart by a bloody civil war. Marxist-led guerrillas and right-wing groups fought one another. During the presidency of Ronald Reagan, the United States provided weapons and training to the Salvadoran army to defeat the guerrillas. In 1984, José Duarte, a moderate, was elected president. But the elections did not stop the killing. By the early 1990s, the civil war had led to the deaths of at least 75,000 people. In 1992, a peace settlement finally brought the war to an end.

Reading Essentials and Study Guide

Chapter 14, Section 2 *(continued)*

In Nicaragua, the Somoza family took control of the government in 1937 and kept control for the next 42 years. The Somoza government had the support of the United States during most of this time. But the Somozas got rich at the nation's expense and used murder and torture against their opponents. By 1979, the United States was no longer willing to support the Somoza government. In that year, Marxist guerrilla forces, known as the Sandinista National Liberation Front, won a number of victories against the government forces. They gained control of the country. Soon, a group called the **contras,** who were opposed to the Sandinistas' policies, began to try to overthrow the new government. The Reagan and Bush administrations in the United States supported the contras, because they were worried about the Sandinistas' ties with the Soviet Union. The war with the contras caused the Sandinistas to lose support. In 1990, the Sandinistas agreed to free elections. They lost to a coalition headed by Violeta Barrios de Chamorro. They lost again in 2001 but remained one of the strongest parties in Nicaragua.

Panama became a nation in 1903, when it broke away from Colombia with the help of the United States. In return for this help, the United States was able to build the Panama Canal. The United States also gained a great deal of influence over the government and economy of Panama. After 1968, power in Panama came into the hands of the military leaders of Panama's National Guard. One of these leaders, Manuel Noriega, took control of Panama in 1983. At first, the United States supported Noriega. But his brutality and involvement with the drug trade turned American leaders against him. In 1989, President George Bush sent U.S. troops to Panama. Noriega was arrested and sent to prison in the United States on charges of drug trafficking.

7. What are the main export products of Central America? How has the export of these products affected the Central American economies?

_____

_____

_____

_____

_____

Reading Essentials and Study Guide

Chapter 14, Section 3

For use with textbook pages 663–667

THE NATIONS OF SOUTH AMERICA

CONTENT VOCABULARY

Desaparecidos "the Disappeared," opponents of the Pinochet regime in Chile who were arrested and never seen again *(page 666)*

cooperative a farm organization owned by and operated for the benefit of the farmers *(page 666)*

Shining Path a radical Communist guerrilla group based in rural areas of Peru whose goal was to smash all authority and create a classless society *(page 666)*

Camisea Gas Project pipeline carrying natural gas from the Amazon through Peru *(page 667)*

DRAWING FROM EXPERIENCE

Have you ever seen the musical or movie *Evita*? Who was Evita? Why do you think a musical was written about her?

In the last section, you read about economic and political crises in Mexico, Cuba, and Central America following World War II. In this section, you will read about economic, political, and social problems in South America during the same period.

ORGANIZING YOUR THOUGHTS

Use the chart below to help you take notes. The military has played an important role in many South American countries. Describe the role of the military in each of the countries in this chart.

> **California History Social Science Standards**
>
> **10.9** Students analyze the international developments in the post-World War II world.
> **10.10** Students analyze instances of nation-building in the contemporary world in two of the following regions or countries: the Middle East, Africa, Mexico, and other parts of Latin America, and China.
>
> **Focuses on:**
> 10.9.1, 10.10.2, 10.10.3

Role of the Military in:	
Argentina	1.
Brazil	2.
Chile	3.
Peru	4.

Reading Essentials and Study Guide

Chapter 14, Section 3 *(continued)*

READ TO LEARN

• Brazil, the Colossus of Latin America *(page 664)*

Like other Latin American countries, Brazil experienced severe economic problems after World War II. When democratic governments were unable to solve these problems, the military stepped in and took control in 1964. The military remained in control for the next 20 years. It set a new economic direction. It reduced government interference in the economy and stressed free market forces. At first, these policies seemed to be working <u>accurately</u>. Beginning in 1968, Brazil experienced an "economic miracle." But ordinary Brazilians benefited very little from this economic growth. The gulf between rich and poor grew even wider.

Rapid growth led to severe inflation. The military government was overwhelmed, and democracy returned in 1985. The new democratic government faced enormous problems. Brazil had a huge foreign debt, severe inflation, and a lack of social unity. In the 1990s, a series of democratically elected presidents managed to restore some stability to Brazil's economy. Dissatisfaction with the gap between rich and poor helped to elect Luiz Inacio Lula da Silva, a left-wing president, in 2002.

> **Academic Vocabulary**
>
> **accurate:** free from error as the result of attention to detail (p. 664)

5. In what ways did Brazil experience an "economic miracle"? In what ways was it not a miracle?

_____

_____

_____

• Argentina and Chile *(page 664)*

Argentina is Latin America's second largest country. For years, it had been ruled by a powerful oligarchy. In 1943, a group of army officials overthrew the oligarchy. Juan Perón, the labor secretary of the new military government, tried to win the support of the workers. He encouraged them to join labor unions. He also increased job benefits and the number of paid vacations and holidays. In 1944, Perón became vice president of the military government. He made sure that people knew that he was responsible for the better conditions for workers. Perón was elected president of Argentina in 1946. His main support came from labor and the urban middle class. To please them, he followed a policy of increased industrialization. He also tried to free Argentina from foreign investors. The government bought the railways and took over the banking, insurance, shipping, and communications industries. Perón's regime was authoritarian. He created Fascist gangs <u>parallel</u> to Hitler's Brownshirts. The gangs used violence to terrify Perón's opponents. Fearing Perón's power, the military overthrew him in September 1955. Perón went into exile in Spain. The military leaders were soon overwhelmed by problems and allowed Perón to return. He was reelected as president in 1973 but died a year later.

> **Academic Vocabulary**
>
> **parallel:** similar or analogous in tendency or development (p. 665)

Reading Essentials and Study Guide

Chapter 14, Section 3 *(continued)*

In 1976, the military once again took control. The new regime allowed no opposition. Perhaps 36,000 people were killed. At the same time, there were serious economic problems. To divert people's attention, the military government invaded the Falkland Islands in April 1982. The Falklands were islands off the coast of Argentina that Great Britain had controlled since the nineteenth century. Great Britain sent ships and troops and took the islands back. The loss made the military look bad. In 1983, Raúl Alfonsín was elected president and worked to restore democratic practices. In 1989, the Perónist Carlos Saúl Menem won the presidential election. This peaceful transfer of power made many people hope that Argentina was moving on a democratic path. Since 2003, the administration of President Nestor Kirchner has seen expanded growth.

In 1970, Salvador Allende, a Marxist, became president of Chile. He tried to create a socialist society by constitutional means. He increased the wages of industrial workers and nationalized the largest corporations. In March 1973, new elections increased the number of Allende's supporters in the Chamber of Deputies. The Chilean army, under the direction of General Augusto Pinochet, was afraid of Allende's power. In September 1973, military forces seized the presidential palace, and shot Allende. The military then set up a dictatorship.

The Pinochet dictatorship was one of the most brutal in Chile's history. Thousands of opponents were imprisoned. Others were tortured and murdered. Thousands were arrested and never seen again—they became known as **"Desaparecidos,"** "the Disappeared." The regime also outlawed all political parties and did away with the Chamber of Deputies. The abuses of human rights led to unrest in the 1980s. In 1989, free presidential elections led to the defeat of Pinochet. Chile moved toward a more democratic system. The current president, Ricardo Lagos, signed a free trade agreement with the United States in 2004.

6. What were some characteristics of Pinochet's regime?

_____

_____

_____

• Colombia and Peru *(page 666)*

The history of Peru has been marked by instability. Peru's dependence on exports has led to extreme ups and downs in the economy. With these ups and downs have come many changes in the government. A military takeover in 1968 brought General Juan Velasco Alvarado to power. He tried to help the peasants. His government took almost 75 percent of the nation's large landed estates and gave the land to peasant **cooperatives** (farm organizations owned by and operated for the benefit of the peasants). The government also nationalized many foreign-owned companies and kept food prices low to help

Reading Essentials and Study Guide

Chapter 14, Section 3 (continued)

urban workers. Economic problems continued, and military leaders removed General Alvarado from power in 1975.

Five years later, the military returned Peru to civilian rule. There were new problems for the civilian government. A radical communist guerrilla group based in rural areas and known as **Shining Path** emerged. It killed mayors, missionaries, priests, and peasants. The goal of Shining Path was to smash all authority and create a classless society. In 1990, Peruvians chose Alberto Fujimori as president. Fujimori promised reforms. Two years later, he suspended the constitution and congress and became a dictator. He began a campaign against Shining Path. He was removed from power in 2000. In June 2001, Alejandro Toledo became Peru's first freely elected president of Native American descent. Toledo presided over the **Camisea Gas Project,** a pipeline to carry natural gas from the Amazon jungle to Lima.

Colombia has had a democratic political system for a long time, but a conservative elite has dominated the government. After World War II, Marxist guerrilla groups began to organize Colombian peasants. The government responded with violence. More than two hundred thousand peasants had been killed by the mid-1960s. Peasants who lived in poverty turned to a new cash crop—coca leaves. Coca leaves are used to make cocaine. The drug trade increased. Drug lords formed cartels (groups of drug businesses). The cartels used bribes and violence to eliminate competitors and to force government cooperation. Attempts to stop the traffic in drugs had little success. The government has begun an aerial eradication program, but Colombia still supplies the majority of cocaine to the international drug market.

Colombia continues to have major economic problems. Unemployment is high (around 17 percent in 2004). Colombia's main exports, coffee and oil, often fluctuate in price, which leads to ups and downs in the economy.

7. How did the drug trade begin in Colombia? What has the government done to try to stop it?

_____

_____

_____

Reading Essentials and Study Guide

Chapter 15, Section 1

For use with textbook pages 677–685

INDEPENDENCE IN AFRICA

CONTENT VOCABULARY

apartheid ("apartness") the system of racial segregation in South Africa from the 1950s to 1991 *(page 678)*

Pan-Africanism the unity of all black Africans, regardless of national boundaries *(page 679)*

DRAWING FROM EXPERIENCE

Have you read any poems by Africans? Have you seen any African art-work? Have you listened to any African music? What do these art forms tell you about African culture?

In this section, you will learn about political, economic, social, and cultural developments in Africa following World War II. Most African nations achieved their independence during this period.

ORGANIZING YOUR THOUGHTS

Use the diagram below to help you take notes. Poverty is widespread in much of Africa. Identify six problems that account for this poverty.

> **California History Social Science Standards**
>
> **10.9** Students analyze the international developments in the post-World War II world.
> **10.10** Students analyze instances of nation-building in the contemporary world in two of the following regions or countries: the Middle East, Africa, Mexico, and other parts of Latin America, and China.
>
> **Focuses on:**
> 10.9.2

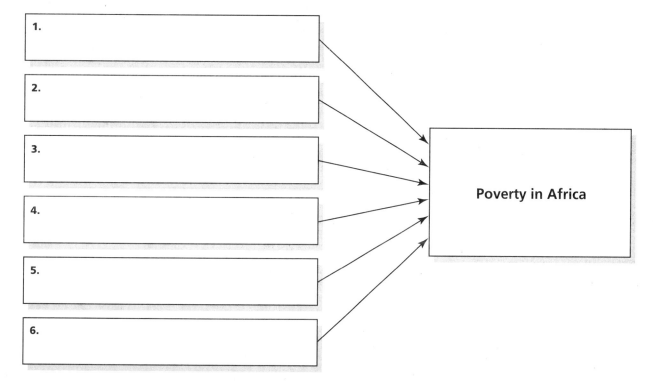

1.

2.

3.

4.

5.

6.

Poverty in Africa

Reading Essentials and Study Guide

Chapter 15, Section 1 *(continued)*

READ TO LEARN

- ## The Transition to Independence *(page 678)*

    After World War II, Europeans realized that colonial rule would have to
end. Great Britain and France both decided to let go of their colonial empires.
In the 1950s and 1960s, most black African nations gained their independence.
In 1957, the Gold Coast was the first former British colony to gain independence. It was renamed Ghana. Nigeria, the Belgian Congo (now the Democratic
Republic of Congo), Kenya, and others followed. Seventeen new African
nations emerged in 1960. Another 11 nations followed between 1961 and 1965.
After a series of guerrilla wars, the Portuguese finally gave up their colonies
of Mozambique and Angola in the 1970s. In North Africa, the French gave
Morocco and Tunisia their independence in 1956. The French chose to keep
control of Algeria, but independence was finally granted in 1962.

    In South Africa, the situation was more complicated. South Africa had a
<u>significant</u> minority of whites who had settled there centuries earlier. By the
1950s, South African whites that were descendants of the Dutch (called
Afrikaners) had laws separating whites and blacks. The result was a system of
racial segregation known as **apartheid** ("apartness"). Blacks had formed the
African National Congress (ANC) in 1912. Its goal was economic and political
reform, but it had little success. Blacks demonstrated against the apartheid
laws, but the white government brutally repressed the demonstrators. After
the arrest of ANC leader Nelson Mandela in 1962, members of the ANC called
for armed resistance to the white government.

Academic Vocabulary
significant: having or likely to have an influence or effect on (p. 678)

7. What was apartheid?

_____

_____

_____

_____

_____

- ## The New Nations *(page 679)*

    Most of the leaders of the newly independent African nations came from
the urban middle class. They had studied in either Europe or the United
States. They spoke and read European languages and believed in democracy.
The views of these leaders on economics were more diverse. Some believed in
Western-style capitalism. Others wanted an "African form of socialism." The
African form of socialism was based on African traditions of community.
Ownership of the country's wealth would be put in the hands of the people.
Some African leaders believed in the dream of **Pan-Africanism** (the unity of
all black Africans, regardless of national boundaries). Pan-Africanism was

Reading Essentials and Study Guide

Chapter 15, Section 1 (continued)

supported by several of the new African leaders, including Léopold Senghor of Senegal, Julius Nyerere of Tanzania, Kwame Nkrumah of Ghana, and Jomo Kenyatta of Kenya. The Organization of African Unity (OAU) was a result of the belief in Pan-Africanism. It was founded in 1963 by the leaders of 32 African nations. In 2002, the African Union (AU) replaced the OAU. The new 53-nation group aims to promote democracy and economic growth in the region.

Independence did not bring economic prosperity to the new African nations. Most of the countries still relied on the export of a single crop or natural resource. When prices for these exports dropped, their economies suffered. Most African nations also had to import technology and manufactured goods from the West. The new nations sometimes created their own problems. Natural resources were spent on military equipment or expensive consumer goods rather than on building the foundations for an industrial economy. Corruption and bribery became common. Population growth also kept many countries from creating modern economies. Drought conditions led to widespread hunger and starvation. Millions fled to neighboring countries in search of food. The Cold War also created problems as the Soviet Union and United States competed for influence in African countries such as Ethiopia, Somalia, Nigeria, and Republic of the Congo. As a result of all these problems, poverty is widespread in Africa. Cities have grown tremendously. They are often surrounded by slums populated by people who came to the cities looking for work. Millions live without water and electricity in their homes. At the same time, a few people enjoy lavish lifestyles. The rich in many East African countries are known as the *wabenzi* (Mercedes-Benz people).

AIDS, or acquired immunodeficiency syndrome, is an epidemic in Africa. About 8 percent of the adult population of Africa south of the Sahara is infected with the HIV virus which causes AIDS. In Swaziland and Botswana, more than 35 percent of the population has HIV. One of the most striking effects of AIDS in Africa is on children and families. Many children have become orphans and the traditional support system of African culture has been overwhelmed. Uganda has made impressive efforts to fight AIDS through a campaign to promote health and sex education.

Many people had hoped that independence would lead to stable political systems based on "one person, one vote." They were soon disappointed. Democratic governments gave way to military regimes and one-party states. Between 1957 and 1982, over 70 leaders of African countries were overthrown by violence. Within many African nations, there were warring ethnic groups. The concept of nationhood was not strong. This was the result of the way that the countries were formed. The boundaries of many African countries had been drawn <u>arbitrarily</u> by colonial powers. Nearly all of these countries included different ethnic, linguistic, and territorial groups. During the late 1960s, civil war tore Nigeria apart. Northerners began to kill the Ibo people,

Academic Vocabulary
arbitrary: not restrained or fixed by law (p. 682)

Reading Essentials and Study Guide

Chapter 15, Section 1 *(continued)*

who fled to their home region in the eastern part of Nigeria. The Ibo declared
the eastern region of Nigeria an independent state called Biafra. After two and
a half years of bloody civil war, Biafra finally surrendered and accepted the
authority of the Nigerian government. In central Africa, fighting between the
Hutu and Tutsi created unstable governments in both Burundi and Rwanda.
In 1994, a Hutu rampage left 500,000 Tutsi dead in Rwanda.

8. What two economic systems have African leaders advocated?

_____

_____

_____

_____

_____

- **New Hopes** *(page 683)*

In recent years, demonstrations have led to the rise of democracies in several
countries. In Uganda, for example, Idi Amin had ruled by terror and repression throughout the 1970s, but he was deposed in 1979. Dictatorships also
came to an end in Ethiopia, Liberia, and Somalia. In these cases, however, the
fall of the dictatorships was followed by civil war.

One of the most remarkable events in recent African history was the election of Nelson Mandela to the presidency of the Republic of South Africa.
Mandela had been sentenced to life imprisonment in 1962 for his activities
with the ANC. He spent almost 26 years in prison. Bishop Desmond Tutu and
others worked to free him and to end apartheid in South Africa. Worldwide
pressure on the white South African government led to reforms and the end
of apartheid laws. In 1990, Mandela was released from prison. In 1993, the
government agreed to hold democratic elections. In 1994, Nelson Mandela
became South Africa's first black president.

9. What factors contributed to the release of Nelson Mandela and the end of apartheid laws in
South Africa?

_____

_____

_____

_____

Reading Essentials and Study Guide

Chapter 15, Section 1 (continued)

• **Society and Culture in Modern Africa** *(page 684)*

Africa is a study in contrasts. Old and new, native and foreign live side by side. There is a constant tension between traditional ways and Western culture. Most African cities look like cities elsewhere in the world. They have high-rises, neon lights, movie theaters, and traffic jams. Outside the cities, where about three-quarters of the people of Africa live, modern influence has had less of an impact. Millions of people live much as their ancestors did, in thatched dwellings without modern plumbing and electricity. They farm, hunt, or raise livestock by traditional methods. They also wear traditional clothing and practice traditional beliefs. Many urban people see rural people as backward. Rural people see the cities as corrupting and destructive to traditional African values and customs.

Independence from colonial powers had an impact on women's roles in Africa. Women were allowed to vote and run for political office. Women dominate some professions, such as teaching, child care, and clerical work, but they do not have the range of career opportunities that men do. Most African women are employed in low-paid positions. In many rural areas, traditional attitudes toward women, including arranged marriages, still prevail.

Africans have kept their native artistic traditions while adapting them to foreign influences. A challenge for many African artists is the need to balance Western techniques and training with the rich heritage of traditional African art forms. In some countries, governments are eager to sell tourists traditional African art.

African writers have often addressed the tensions that modern Africans face. The conflicting demands of town versus country and native versus foreign were the themes of most of the best-known works of the 1960s and 1970s. For example, the novels of Chinua Achebe show the problems of Africans caught up in the conflict between traditional and Western values.

10. How do most of the people of Africa live?

_____

_____

_____

_____

_____

Reading Essentials and Study Guide

Chapter 15, Section 2

For use with textbook pages 688–692

CONFLICT IN THE MIDDLE EAST

CONTENT VOCABULARY

Pan-Arabism Arab unity, regardless of national boundaries *(page 690)*

OPEC the Organization of Petroleum Exporting Countries formed in 1960 by several Arab oil-producing nations to control the price of oil *(page 691)*

intifada ("uprising") militant movement that arose during the 1980s among supporters of the Palestine Liberation Organization living in Israel *(page 691)*

DRAWING FROM EXPERIENCE

Have you ever looked at a world map to find the Middle East? The Middle Eastern countries are located on two continents. What are the two continents? Why do geographers classify countries from two different continents into the same region (the Middle East)? What do these countries have in common?

In the last section, you read about developments in Africa following World War II. In this section, you will read about developments in the Middle East during this time. There have been many armed conflicts in this region.

> **California History
> Social Science Standards**
>
> **10.9** Students analyze the international developments in the post-World War II world.
> **10.10** Students analyze instances of nation-building in the contemporary world in two of the following regions or countries: the Middle East, Africa, Mexico, and other parts of Latin America, and China.
>
> **Focuses on:**
> 10.9.6

ORGANIZING YOUR THOUGHTS

Use the chart below to help you take notes. Identify the causes and outcomes of each conflict in this chart.

Middle East Conflict	Causes	Outcomes
Suez War of 1956	1.	2.
Six-Day War of 1967	3.	4.
Arab-Israeli War of 1973	5.	6.
Iraq-Iran War (1980s)	7.	8.

Reading Essentials and Study Guide

Chapter 15, Section 2 *(continued)*

READ TO LEARN

• The Middle East and Palestine *(page 689)*

In the Middle East, World War II led to the emergence of new independent states. Syria and Lebanon gained their independence near the end of World War II. Jordan achieved self-rule soon after the war. These new states were predominantly Muslim.

In the years between the two world wars, many Jews had immigrated to Palestine. Tensions between Jews and Arabs had increased during the 1930s. Great Britain governed Palestine under a United Nations mandate. It had limited Jewish immigration into the area and had rejected proposals for an independent Jewish state in Palestine. As a result of the Holocaust, sympathy for the Jewish cause grew following World War II. In 1948, a United Nations resolution divided Palestine into a Jewish state and an Arab state. The Jews in Palestine proclaimed the state of Israel on May 14, 1948. Israel's Arab neighbors saw the new state as a betrayal of the Palestinian people, most of whom were Muslim. Several Arab countries invaded Israel. The invasion failed, but the Arab states still refused to recognize Israel's right to exist. As a result of the division of Palestine, hundreds of thousands of Palestinians fled to neighboring Arab countries. Other Palestinians came under Israeli rule.

In the early 1950s, Colonel Gamal Abdel Nasser took control of the Egyptian government. On July 26, 1956, Nasser seized the Suez Canal Company, which had been under British and French control. Great Britain and France decided to strike back. Israel quickly joined them. The three nations launched an attack on Egypt. This started the Suez War of 1956. The United States and the Soviet Union supported Nasser and forced Britain, France, and Israel to withdraw their troops from Egypt.

Nasser emerged from the conflict as a powerful leader. He now began to promote **Pan-Arabism** (Arab unity). In February 1958, Egypt united with Syria to form the United Arab Republic (UAR). Nasser was named the first president of this new state. Egypt and Syria hoped that the union would eventually include all Arab states. But many other Arab leaders were suspicious of Pan-Arabism. Oil-rich Arab states were concerned that they would have to share revenues with poorer states in the Middle East. It was Nasser's <u>motive</u> to share these resources. In 1961, military leaders took over Syria and withdrew the country from its union with Egypt.

Academic Vocabulary
motive: something, like a need or desire, that causes a person to act (p. 690)

During the late 1950s and 1960s, the dispute between Israel and other states in the Middle East became more heated. In 1967, Nasser imposed a blockade against Israeli shipping through the Gulf of Aqaba. He also said that he was ready to confront Israel. Fearing attack, Israel launched air strikes against Egypt and several of its Arab neighbors on June 5, 1967. Israeli planes wiped out most of the Egyptian air force. Israeli armies broke the blockade and occupied the Sinai Peninsula. Israel also seized territory on the West Bank of the Jordan River, occupied Jerusalem, and took control of the Golan Heights.

Reading Essentials and Study Guide

Chapter 15, Section 2 *(continued)*

During this Six-Day War, Israel tripled the size of its territory. Over the next few years, Arab states demanded the return of the occupied territories. Nasser died in 1970 and was succeeded by Anwar el-Sadat. In 1973, Arab forces led by Sadat launched a new attack against Israel. This conflict was ended in 1974 by a cease-fire agreement negotiated by the United Nations.

The war was having indirect effects in Western nations. A number of Arab oil-producing states had formed the Organization of Petroleum Exporting Countries **(OPEC)** in 1960 to gain control over oil prices. During the 1973 war, some OPEC nations announced large increases in the price of oil to foreign countries. The price hikes and cuts in oil production led to oil shortages in the United States and Europe. In 1977, U.S. president Jimmy Carter began to push for a peace agreement between Arabs and Israelis. In September 1978, Carter met with President Sadat of Egypt and Israeli <u>Prime</u> Minister Menachem Begin at Camp David. The result was the Camp David Accords, an agreement to sign an Israeli-Egyptian peace treaty. Sadat and Begin signed the treaty in March 1979. It ended the war between Egypt and Israel.

Academic Vocabulary
prime: first in rank, authority, or significant (p. 691)

In 1964, the Egyptians formed the Palestine Liberation Organization (PLO) to represent the interests of the Palestinians. The PLO believed that only the Palestinian peoples had the right to create a state in Palestine. A guerrilla movement called al-Fatah began to launch terrorist attacks on Israeli territory. The PLO leader Yasir Arafat headed it. Militancy in the early 1980s led to a movement called the *intifada* ("uprising") among PLO supporters living in the territories occupied by Israel since the 1967 Arab-Israeli war.

Finally, in 1993, Israel and the PLO reached an agreement calling for Palestinian autonomy in certain areas of Israel. In return, the PLO recognized the Israeli state. Yasir Arafat became the head of the semi-independent area known as the Palestinian Authority.

9. What is the PLO? What agreement did it reach with Israel in 1993?

_____

_____

_____

Reading Essentials and Study Guide

Chapter 15, Section 2 (continued)

• Turmoil in Iran and Iraq (page 691)

The leadership of Shah Mohammad Reza Pahlavi and revenue from oil helped Iran to become a rich country. But there was much opposition to the shah in Iran. Devout Muslims looked with distaste at the new Iranian civilization. In their eyes, it was based on greed and materialism, which they identified with American influence. Leading the opposition to the shah was the Ayatollah Ruhollah Khomeini, a member of the Muslim clergy. In 1979, the shah's government collapsed and was replaced by an Islamic republic. The new government, led by Ayatollah Khomeini, began to restore Islamic law. Anti-American sentiments led to the taking of 52 American hostages from the United States embassy in Tehran. After the death of Khomeini in 1989, a new government under President Hashemi Rafsanjani began to loosen control over personal expression and social activities. But a new wave of government repression began in the mid-1990s.

To the west of Iran was the nation of Iraq, led by Saddam Hussein. Iran and Iraq have a history of conflict, made worse by their religious differences. The Iranians are mostly Shiite Muslims, while the leaders of Iraq are predominantly Sunni Muslims. In 1980, Saddam Hussein attacked Iran, using brutal tactics including the use of poison gas against civilians. A cease-fire was signed in 1988.

10. Why do Iran and Iraq have a poor relationship?

_____

_____

_____

Reading Essentials and Study Guide

Chapter 15, Section 3

For use with textbook pages 693–699

THE CHALLENGE OF TERRORISM

CONTENT VOCABULARY

Irish Republican Army (IRA) militant nationalists who want to unite Northern Ireland *(page 694)*

state-sponsored terrorism terrorists who work for one nation to undermine the government of another *(page 694)*

al-Qaeda terrorist group led by Osama bin Laden which recruited Muslims and sent money and arms to Afghanistan to support the Afghan resistance *(page 696)*

Taliban a Muslim fundamentalist group *(page 696)*

Patriot Act an antiterrorist bill passed after 9/11 which allows secret searches to avoid tipping off terrorism suspects. The law made it easier to wiretap suspects and to track e-mail, seize voice mail, and monitor library records *(page 697)*

DRAWING FROM EXPERIENCE

Where were you when you heard about the attacks on the World Trade Center Towers? How did this event affect your life?

In the last section, you read about economic and political developments in the Middle East in the late twentieth century. In this section you will read how the growth of terrorism has had a great impact on Western countries.

> **California History Social Science Standards**
>
> **10.10** Students analyze instances of nation-building in the contemporary world in two of the following regions or countries: the Middle East, Africa, Mexico, and other parts of Latin America, and China.

ORGANIZING YOUR THOUGHTS

Use the chart below to help you take notes. Terrorists groups have caused destruction in order to achieve their goals.

	Country	Goals
Irish Republican Army	1.	4.
Al-Qaeda	2.	5.
Taliban	3.	6.

Reading Essentials and Study Guide

Chapter 15, Section 3 *(continued)*

• Modern Terrorism *(page 694)*

Acts of terrorism have become a part of modern society. Terrorists kill civilians, take hostages, and hijack airplanes to draw attention to their demands or to achieve their goals. Some terrorists are militant nationalists who wish to create separate states. One example is the **Irish Republican Army (IRA).** Its goal is to unite Northern Ireland, which is ruled by Great Britain, with the Irish Republic. Since the 1970s, IRA terrorists have been responsible for the deaths of thousands of people. **State-sponsored terrorism** is another form of terrorism. Some militant governments have provided support to terrorist organizations. Iraq, Iran, Libya, Syria, and North Korea are some examples.

Analysts give many causes for the growth of modern terrorism. Some say it is rooted in the clash of modern and Islamic cultures. Others note that Christians and Muslims have between hostile to each other for centuries. Others say that poverty and ignorance are at the root, and still others say terrorism is a symptom of the Israeli-Palestinian conflict. Most terrorist acts since World War II have been carried out by Middle Eastern groups against Western countries. The United States has invested heavily in the Middle East oil industry. While this brought great wealth to the ruling families, most Middle Eastern citizens remained poor. Some Muslims feared interaction with the West would weaken their religion and way of life. Fundamentalist Muslims began organizing movements to overthrow their pro-Western governments. The Ayatollah Khomeini attempted to make a conservative Islamic society in Iran. Some people believe most Muslims are extremists, but in fact the militants are in a minority.

After World War II, Afghanistan looked to the Soviet Union for economic assistance. By 1978, the Soviets controlled Afghanistan. The new communist leaders were opposed by Afghans who wanted an Islamic state. In 1979, the Soviets invaded Afghanistan. The United States feared this Soviet expansion and supported the Afghans against the Soviets. Osama bin Laden, a wealthy Saudi Arabian, used his wealth to support Afghan resistance. He founded **al-Qaeda** in 1988, which recruited Muslims and sent money and arms to Afghanistan. Bin Laden dedicated himself to driving Westerners out of Muslim countries.

Reading Essentials and Study Guide

Chapter 15, Section 3 *(continued)*

When the **Taliban,** a Muslim fundamentalist group, took control of Afghanistan in 1996, bin Laden began using Afghanistan to train al-Qaeda recruits. In 1998, bin Laden's followers set off bombs at the American embassies in Kenya and Tanzania, killing 224 people. U.S. president Bill Clinton ordered an attack on terrorist facilities in Afghanistan and Sudan, but bin Laden was not deterred. In 2000, al-Qaeda terrorists attacked the USS *Cole*, which was docked near Yemen.

7. Why did the United States enter the conflict in Afghanistan?

_____

_____

_____

_____

- **The Attack of 9/11** *(page 697)*

One of the most destructive acts of terrorism occurred on September 11, 2001. Terrorists, directed by al-Qaeda, hijacked four commercial U.S. jets. They flew two of the airplanes into the World Trade Center towers in New York City. They flew the third airplane into the Pentagon in Arlington, Virginia. The fourth plane was diverted by heroic passengers and crashed in an isolated area of Pennsylvania. Thousands of people were killed, including all of the people aboard the airplanes.

The U.S. government gathered evidence that indicated that the acts had been carried out by al-Qaeda, the terrorist organization of Osama bin Laden.

In October 2001, President George W. Bush led a coalition of nations in a war against the Taliban. The Northern Alliance, an Afghan coalition that had fought the Taliban for several years, led the ground attack. By December, the Taliban government had collapsed. Afghan leaders selected Hamid Karzai as the new president, but Karzai faced many challenges, including poverty and building political agreement. In the United States, President Bush asked Congress to pass legislation to help track down terrorist suspects.

Reading Essentials and Study Guide

Chapter 15, Section 3 (continued)

The **Patriot Act** was passed in October 2001. It allowed secret searches, to avoid alerting terrorism suspects. In November 2002, Congress established the Department of Homeland Security, to coordinate the dozens of <u>federal</u> agencies, such as the Coast Guard, Customs, and Immigration and Naturalization.

8. What was the purpose of the Patriot Act?

_____

_____

_____

_____

> **Academic Vocabulary**
> **federal:** an agency or organization that operates on behalf of the government (p. 697)

- **The Iraq Factor** *(page 698)*

In January 2002, President Bush told the American people that countries that sponsored terrorism were suspected of having weapons of mass destruction, which could kill thousands of people all at once. Iraq was considered an immediate threat, because Saddam Hussein had used chemical weapons in the past. In 1991, U.N. inspectors learned that Iraq had developed biological weapons and was working on a nuclear bonb. The U.N. Security Council called for Iraq to disarm its weapons programs, but Iraq repeatedly refused. In 2002, President Bush demanded that Iraq give up weapons of mass destruction. Bush asked Congress to authorize the use of force against Iraq. On March 20, 2003, a U.S.-led coalition attacked Iraq. Within six weeks, coalition forces gained control of the country. The fighting continued, however. Americans did not find any evidence of weapons of mass destruction, perhaps due to flawed information given to the president. Establishing a new government in Iraq was difficult because Iraqi society was composed of three very different groups: Shiite Muslims, Sunni Muslims, and ethnic Kurds. In December 2003 Saddam Hussein was captured. Guerrillas who feared they would have no power in an American-<u>designed</u> government continued to attack coalition forces and the newly organized Iraqi police. On June 28, 2004 the U.S. officially transferred sovereignty to Iraq, with Iyad Allawi as the prime minister.

> **Academic Vocabulary**
> **design:** to create, fashion, execute, or construct according to plan (p. 699)

9. Why was establishing a new government in Iraq difficult?

_____

_____

_____

Reading Essentials and Study Guide

Chapter 16, Section 1

For use with textbook pages 709–715

COMMUNIST CHINA

CONTENT VOCABULARY

commune in China during the 1950s, a group of collective farms each of which contained more than 30,000 people who lived and worked together *(page 710)*

permanent revolution an atmosphere of constant revolutionary fervor favored by Mao Zedong to enable China to overcome the past and achieve the final stage of communism *(page 710)*

one-child policy *(page 713)*

DRAWING FROM EXPERIENCE

Do you have any relatives who fought in the Korean War? What caused the war between North and South Korea?

In this section, you will learn how the Communist Party came to power in China and the effects that communism has had on China. You will also learn how Cold War tensions led to the Korean War.

ORGANIZING YOUR THOUGHTS

Use the chart below to help you take notes. Describe the Communist programs in this chart and list the outcomes of these programs.

> **California History Social Science Standards**
>
> **10.9** Students analyze the international developments in the post-World War II world. **10.10** Students analyze instances of nation-building in the contemporary world in two of the following regions or countries: the Middle East, Africa, Mexico, and other parts of Latin America, and China.
>
> **Focuses on:**
> 10.9.3, 10.9.4

Communist Program	Description	Outcomes
collectivization	1.	2.
Great Leap Forward	3.	4.
Cultural Revolution	5.	6.
Four Modernizations	7.	8.

Reading Essentials and Study Guide

Chapter 16, Section 1 (continued)

READ TO LEARN

• The Leadership of Chairman Mao (page 710)

By 1945, there were two Chinese governments. The Nationalist government of Chiang Kai-shek was based in southern and central China. The United States supported it. The Communist government under Mao Zedong was based in North China. In 1945, war broke out between the Nationalists and the Communists. Many peasants joined Mao's People's Liberation Army. By the spring of 1949, the People's Liberation Army had defeated the Nationalists. Chiang Kai-shek and his followers fled to the island of Taiwan, which they declared the Republic of China.

The Communist Party now ruled China (called the People's Republic of China). In 1955, the Chinese government began a program to build a socialist society. Lands were taken from wealthy landlords and given to poor peasants. About two-thirds of the peasants received land under the new program. Most industry and commerce was nationalized. Most of the farmland was collectivized. Chinese leaders hoped that collective farms would increase food production. They hoped that this would allow more people to work in industry. But food production did not grow.

To speed up economic growth, Mao began a radical program, known as the Great Leap Forward, in 1958. Collective farms were combined into vast **communes.** Each commune contained more than thirty thousand people who lived and worked together. The Great Leap Forward was a disaster. The peasants hated the new system. Bad planning and bad weather made food production decline. As a result, at least 16 people died of starvation. In 1960, the government began to break up the communes and return to collective farms and some private plots.

In spite of the commune failure, Mao still dreamed of the final stage of communism—a classless society. Mao believed that only **permanent revolution** (an atmosphere of constant revolutionary fervor) would make it possible for the Chinese to reach this final stage. In 1966, Mao launched the Great Proletarian Cultural Revolution. ("Proletarian" means the working class.) A collection of Mao's thoughts, called the *Little Red Book,* was considered the most important source of knowledge in all areas.

To promote the Cultural Revolution, the Red Guards were formed. These were revolutionary groups that were made up primarily of young people. Red Guards were sent throughout the country to eliminate the "Four Olds"—old ideas, old culture, old customs, and old habits. The Red Guard destroyed temples, books written by foreigners, and foreign music. People who had not followed Mao's plan were attacked. Intellectuals and artists accused of being pro-Western were especially open to attack. But there were groups within the country that did not share Mao's desire for permanent revolution. Many people were upset by the Red Guards' attacks and began to turn against the movement.

Reading Essentials and Study Guide

Chapter 16, Section 1 *(continued)*

9. What was considered the most important source of knowledge during the Cultural Revolution?

_____

_____

_____

_____

_____

• **China After Mao** *(page 712)*

In 1976, Mao Zedong died at the age of 82. A group of practical reformers seized power and brought the Cultural Revolution to an end. Deng Xiaoping led them. Under Deng, the government followed a policy called the Four Modernizations. This policy focused on four areas—industry, agriculture, technology, and national defense. Deng wanted to <u>release</u> China from its isolation. The government invited foreign investors to China. Thousands of students were sent to other countries to study science, technology, and modern business techniques. A new agricultural policy was also begun. Collective farms could now lease land to peasant families who paid rent to the collective. Anything produced on the land above the amount of the rent could be sold on the private market. Overall, modernization worked. Industrial output skyrocketed. Per capita (per person) income doubled during the 1980s. The standard of living increased for most people.

> **Academic Vocabulary**
>
> **release:** to set free from restraint, confinement, or servitude (p. 712)

As more Chinese people began to study abroad, more information about Western society reached educated people. But the new leaders did not allow criticism of the Communist Party. People who called for democracy were often sent to prison. In the late 1980s, high inflation led to discontent, especially in the cities. Corruption and special treatment for officials also led to criticism of the government. In May 1989, students protested the corruption and demanded the resignation of China's Communist party leaders. Many people in the cities supported the students. They led mass demonstrations in Tiananmen Square in Beijing. Deng Xiaoping saw the students' desire for democracy as a demand for the end of the Communist Party. He ordered tanks and troops into Tiananmen Square to crush the demonstrators. Between 700 and 3,000 were killed and many more <u>injured</u>.

> **Academic Vocabulary**
>
> **injure:** to physically hurt someone (p. 713)

Throughout the 1990s, China's human rights violations and its determination to unify with Taiwan strained its relationship with the West. China's increasing military power has also caused concern in other countries. However, in 2001, China joined the World Trade Organization.

Reading Essentials and Study Guide

Chapter 16, Section 1 *(continued)*

10. How were calls for democracy treated under Deng Xiaoping?

_____

_____

_____

• **Chinese Society Under Communism** *(page 713)*

The Chinese Communist Party wanted to create a new kind of citizen. These new citizens would be expected to contribute their utmost for the good of all. Women's roles were changed. Women were now allowed to take part in politics. In 1950, a new marriage law guaranteed women equal rights with men. The Communists also tried to destroy the influence of the traditional family. Loyalty to the family had always been an important part of the Confucian social order. The Communists thought that loyalty to family would interfere with loyalty to the state. During the Cultural Revolution, children were encouraged to spy on their parents. They were supposed to report any comments that their parents made that criticized the system.

After the death of Mao, there was a shift away from revolutionary fervor and a return to family traditions. For most people, this shift meant better living conditions. The new attitudes also were reflected in people's clothing. Under Mao, people had worn only baggy "Mao suits." After Mao's death, young Chinese people began to wear jeans, sneakers, and sweat suits.

11. What was the attitude of the Communists toward the family?

_____

_____

_____

• **China and the World: The Cold War in Asia** *(page 714)*

Korea had been part of the Japanese Empire from 1905 until 1945. In August 1945, the Soviet Union and the United States agreed to divide Korea into two zones at the 38th parallel. The original plan was to hold elections after the end of World War II to reunify Korea. But the relationship between the United States and the Soviet Union grew worse after the war. Two separate governments were set up in Korea—a Communist one in the north and an anti-Communist one in the south.

North Korean troops invaded South Korea on June 25, 1950. U.S. President Harry Truman sent U.S. troops to fight the North Koreans. The United Nations supported this move. In October 1950, UN forces (mostly Americans)

Reading Essentials and Study Guide

Chapter 16, Section 1 *(continued)*

marched across the 38th parallel. Their goal was the reunification of Korea. The Chinese sent hundreds of thousands of Chinese troops into North Korea and pushed UN forces back across the 38th parallel. The fighting continued for three more years, but there was no final victory. An armistice was signed in 1953. The 38th parallel remained the dividing line between North and South Korea.

In 1950, China had signed a pact of friendship and cooperation with the Soviet Union. Some Americans and other Westerners began to worry about a Communist desire for world domination. These fears led to China's isolation from the major Western powers. China was forced to rely almost entirely on the Soviet Union for technological and economic aid. In the late 1950s, however, relations between China and the Soviet Union began to deteriorate. In the 1960s, Chinese and Soviet military forces often clashed at the border between the two countries. Chinese leaders decided to improve relations with the United States. In 1972, President Richard Nixon made a state visit to China. He was the first U.S. president to visit the People's Republic of China. In 1979, diplomatic relations were established with the United States. Chinese relations with the Soviet Union also gradually improved during the 1980s. By the 1990s, China had an active role in Asian affairs.

12. How did Korea become two countries?

_____

_____

_____

_____

_____

Reading Essentials and Study Guide

Chapter 16, Section 2

For use with textbook pages 720–725

INDEPENDENT STATES IN SOUTH AND SOUTHEAST ASIA

CONTENT VOCABULARY

outsourcing a practice where companies send certain jobs, such as data entry or customer service, to countries with lower wages *(page 722)*

stalemate the condition that exists when neither of two opposing sides is able to make significant gains *(page 724)*

discrimination prejudice, usually based on race, religion, class, sex, or age *(page 725)*

DRAWING FROM EXPERIENCE

Do you know anyone who fought in the Vietnam War? Do you know anyone who protested the war? Why did the U.S. send troops to Vietnam?

In the last section, you read about Communist China and the Korean War. In this section, you will learn how India, Pakistan, and the countries of Southeast Asia gained their independence. You will also learn about the problems these countries have faced since gaining their independence. Many of these problems have led to armed conflicts, including the Vietnam War.

> **California History
> Social Science Standards**
>
> **10.9** Students analyze the international developments in the post-World War II world.
> **10.11** Students analyze the integration of countries into the world economy and the information, technological, and communications revolutions (e.g., television, satellites, computers).
>
> **Focuses on:**
> 10.9.3

ORGANIZING YOUR THOUGHTS

Use the chart below to help you take notes. For each of the countries in this chart, describe some of the challenges and conflicts that they have faced since the end of World War II.

Country	Challenges and Conflicts
India	**1.**
Pakistan	**2.**
Philippines	**3.**
Vietnam	**4.**

Reading Essentials and Study Guide

Chapter 16, Section 2 *(continued)*

READ TO LEARN

• British India Divided: India and Pakistan *(page 721)*

When British rule in India ended, the leaders of India realized that India would have to be divided into two countries, one Hindu (India) and one Muslim (Pakistan). Pakistan consisted of two regions separated by India. One part, West Pakistan, was to the northwest of India. The other, East Pakistan, was to the northeast. On August 15, 1947, India and Pakistan became independent. Millions of Hindus and Muslims fled across the new borders—Hindus to India and Muslims to Pakistan. Violence broke out, and more than a million people were killed. One of those killed was Mohandas Gandhi, who was assassinated by a Hindu militant on January 30, 1948.

The Indian National Congress began to rule India. It was renamed the Congress Party. Jawaharlal Nehru was the new prime minister. He was a popular figure with strong ideas about the future of India. Nehru's vision of the new India combined a parliamentary form of government with a moderate socialist economic structure. The government took over the ownership of major industries, utilities, and transportation. Private enterprise was permitted at the local level. Farmland remained in private hands. Industrial production almost tripled between 1950 and 1965.

Nehru died in 1964. In 1966, the leaders of the Congress Party selected Nehru's daughter, Indira Gandhi, as the new prime minister. She held that position until 1984. India had many problems during this period. Its population growth was one of the most serious problems. In spite of government efforts, India was unable to control this growth. One result was poverty for many people. Millions lived in vast city slums. Another problem was ethnic and religious conflict. This conflict involved the Sikhs. The Sikhs were followers of a religion based on both Hindu and Muslim ideas. Many Sikhs lived in a province called the Punjab. Many of them wanted this province to be independent from India. Gandhi refused to allow this. In 1984, she used military force against Sikh rebels. More than 450 Sikhs were killed. Two Sikhs in Gandhi's bodyguard assassinated her in retaliation for the killings.

Gandhi's son Rajiv replaced his mother as prime minister in 1984. He began to move the government in new directions, encouraging private enterprise and foreign investments. His efforts led to growth in India's middle class. In 1991, he was assassinated while campaigning for reelection. Since then, Gandhi's party, the Congress Party, has been forced to compete with new political parties.

Tensions between Hindus and Muslims continue to disturb India's stability. These religious differences have fueled a long-term dispute over Kashmir, a territory located between India and Pakistan. Both countries want to control Kashmir. In 1998 this conflict became an international concern when both nations tested nuclear weapons. By 2002, tensions had eased.

Reading Essentials and Study Guide

Chapter 16, Section 2 *(continued)*

Pakistan was a completely new nation when it gained its independence in 1947. During its early years, there were intense conflicts within the country. The division between East and West Pakistan was a major source of conflict. The government was based in West Pakistan. Many people in East Pakistan felt that the government ignored their needs. In 1971, East Pakistan declared its independence. After a brief civil war, it became the new nation of Bangladesh.

Bangladesh and Pakistan have both had problems establishing stable governments. In both nations, military officials have often seized control of the government. Both nations are also very poor.

5. Why was India divided into two countries?

_____

_____

_____

_____

_____

Reading Essentials and Study Guide

Chapter 16, Section 2 *(continued)*

• **Southeast Asia** *(page 723)*

In July 1946, the Philippines became independent of the United States. Great Britain also ended its colonial rule in Southeast Asia. Burma became independent in 1948. Malaya became independent in 1957. The Netherlands and France were less willing to give up their colonial empires. Nationalists in Indonesia tried to set up an independent republic, but the Dutch suppressed it. The Indonesian Communist Party then tried to seize power. The United States pressured the Netherlands to grant independence to the non-Communist Nationalist Party. In 1949, the Netherlands recognized the new Republic of Indonesia.

In Vietnam, the leading force in the movement to end colonial rule was the Communist Party, led by Ho Chi Minh. In August 1945, the Vietminh seized control of most of Vietnam. The Vietminh was an alliance of forces under Communist leadership. Ho Chi Minh was elected president of a new republic in Hanoi. But France refused to accept the new government and seized the southern part of the country. France fought the Vietminh for control of Vietnam, but France was unable to regain control. In 1954, France agreed to a peace settlement. Vietnam was divided into two parts. In the north, the Communists were based in Hanoi. In the south, the non-Communists were based in Saigon. Both sides agreed to hold elections in two years to create a single government. But the conflict continued. The United States began to provide aid to South Vietnam. In spite of this aid, the Viet Cong were on the verge of seizing control of the entire country by early 1965. The Viet Cong were South Vietnamese Communist guerrillas, who were supported by military units from North Vietnam.

In 1965, President Lyndon Johnson decided to send U.S. troops to South Vietnam to prevent the Communists from taking control. By the end of the 1960s, the war had reached a **stalemate** (neither side was able to make significant gains). President Richard Nixon reached an agreement with North Vietnam in 1973 that allowed the United States to withdraw its forces. Within two years, Communist armies had reunited Vietnam under Communist control. By the end of 1975, both Laos and Cambodia had Communist governments. In Cambodia, the dictator Pol Pot, leader of the Khmer Rouge, massacred more than a million Cambodians. But the Communist victories in Indochina did not lead to the "falling dominoes" that many U.S. leaders had feared.

Many of the leaders of the newly independent states in Southeast Asia hoped to form democratic, capitalist systems. By the end of the 1950s, hopes for economic growth had failed. Disputes within the new countries weakened democratic governments. This opened the door to both military and one-party regimes. In more recent years, some Southeast Asian societies have shown signs of moving toward more democratic governments. In the Philippines, Ferdinand Marcos came to power in 1965. Under Marcos, fraud and corruption were widespread. Marcos was accused of <u>involvement</u> in the

Academic Vocabulary
involvement: participation (p. 725)

Reading Essentials and Study Guide

Chapter 16, Section 2 *(continued)*

killing of Benigno Aquino, a leader of the opposition. An uprising forced
Marcos to flee the country. In 1986, Corazon Aquino, wife of the murdered
leader, became president and worked for democratic reforms. In 2001
President Joseph Estrada was forced from office over charges that he had
plundered the economy. Muslim terrorists have been a persistent challenge
for the Philippine government.

Women's roles in South and Southeast Asia have changed considerably.
After independence, India's leaders tried to expand women's rights. The constitution of 1950 forbade **discrimination** (prejudicial treatment) based on
<u>gender</u>. It also called for equal pay for equal work. Child marriage was out-
lawed. Women were encouraged to attend school and to get jobs. In Southeast
Asia, nearly all of the newly independent states gave women full legal and
political rights.

Academic Vocabulary
gender: the behavioral, cultural, or psychological traits typically associated with one sex (p. 725)

6. How have women's roles changed in South and Southeast Asia?

_____

_____

_____

_____

_____

Reading Essentials and Study Guide

Chapter 16, Section 3

For use with textbook pages 726–733

JAPAN AND THE PACIFIC

CONTENT VOCABULARY

occupied held by a foreign power *(page 727)*

state capitalism an economic system in which the central government plays an active role in the economy, establishing price and wage policies and subsidizing vital industries *(page 728)*

DRAWING FROM EXPERIENCE

Do you or your family own any products that were made in Japan? What are these products?

In the last two sections, you read about changes in China, India, Pakistan, and Southeast Asia since the end of World War II. In this section, you will read about changes in Japan and other countries of the Pacific. Many of these countries have created successful industrial societies.

ORGANIZING YOUR THOUGHTS

Use the diagram below to help you take notes. List six factors that have contributed to Japan's economic success.

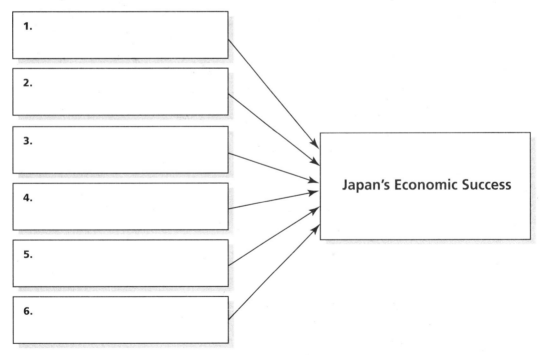

1.	
2.	
3.	
4.	Japan's Economic Success
5.	
6.	

California History Social Science Standards

10.9 Students analyze the international developments in the post-World War II world.
10.11 Students analyze the integration of countries into the world economy and the information, technological, and communications revolutions (e.g., television, satellites, computers).

Focuses on:
10.9.1, 10.9.3

Reading Essentials and Study Guide

Chapter 16, Section 3 *(continued)*

READ TO LEARN

- ## The Allied Occupation *(page 727)*

From 1945 to 1952, Japan was an **occupied** country. Its lands were held and controlled by Allied military forces. An Allied administration governed Japan. This administration was under the command of U.S. General Douglas MacArthur. A new constitution was created. In it, Japan agreed to keep its armed forces at levels that were only enough for self-defense. The new constitution also set up a democratic system and reduced the power of the emperor. It guaranteed basic civil rights and gave women the right to vote.

On September 8, 1951, the United States and other World War II allies signed a peace treaty that gave Japan its independence. Japan and the United States also signed an alliance in which the Japanese agreed that the United States could keep military bases in Japan.

7. What were some of the provisions of Japan's new constitution?

_____

_____

_____

_____

_____

- ## The Japanese Miracle *(page 727)*

After World War II, Japan quickly became an economic giant. This has often been described as the "Japanese miracle." Japan made a dramatic recovery from the war. Several factors contributed to this "miracle." The government played a major role. Japan's new constitution provided for universal suffrage and a balance of power between the executive, legislative, and judicial branches of government. Today Japan is a stable democratic society. The current Japanese political system still has some of the features of Japan's political system under the Meiji. Japan has a multiparty system with two major parties, the Liberal Democrats and the Socialists. But the Liberal Democrats have dominated the government. Key decisions were made by a small group within this party. A change took place in 1993, when the Liberal Democrats were defeated. Mirohiro Hosokawa was elected prime minister and promised to clean up politics.

The central government plays an active role in the economy. It establishes price and wage policies and <u>subsidizes</u> industries. The government's role in the economy is often cited as a key reason for the efficiency of Japanese industry. Japan's economic system has been described as **"state capitalism."** During the occupation of Japan, a land reform program was put in place. Under this

Academic Vocabulary
subsidize: to aid or promote a private enterprise with public money (p. 728)

Reading Essentials and Study Guide

Chapter 16, Section 3 *(continued)*

program, lands were sold on easy credit terms to the tenants. The reform program created a strong class of farmers. Today Japan is the greatest exporting nation in the world. Its per capita income is among the highest in the world.

Cultural factors also help to explain Japan's economic success. The Japanese are group oriented and find it easy to cooperate with one another. They are also hardworking and are inclined to save rather than to buy. These characteristics have produced high savings rates and labor productivity.

There are other, more practical reasons for Japan's success. Japan's industries were destroyed in World War II, so Japan was forced to build entirely new, modern factories. Japanese workers spend considerably more time at their jobs than workers in other countries. Corporations reward innovation and maintain good management-labor relations. Finally, some people believe that Japan uses unfair trade practices—that it sells goods at prices below cost to break into foreign markets and restricts imports from other countries.

There have been major social and cultural changes in Japan since the end of World War II. A new educational system removed all references to patriotism and loyalty to the emperor. It also stressed individualism. Women were given the right to vote and were encouraged to enter politics. But many of the distinctive characteristics of traditional Japanese society still exist. Emphasis on the work ethic is still strong. The tradition of hard work is stressed in the educational system. The subordinate position of women has not been entirely eliminated. Women are now legally protected against discrimination in employment, but very few have reached senior levels in business, education, or politics. Women now make up more than 40 percent of the workforce, but most are in retail or service jobs. Their average salary is only about 60 percent that of men.

After the Japanese defeat in World War II, many of the writers who had been active before the war continued to write. But their writing was more sober now. Several writers committed suicide. Since the 1970s, there has been a huge production of books. In 1975, Japan produced twice as much fiction as the United States. Current Japanese authors were raised in cities and soaked up movies, television, and rock music. These writers deal with the concerns of all wealthy industrialized nations. Haruki Murakami is one of Japan's most popular authors. He was one of the first writers to give up the somber style of the postwar period.

8. What characteristics of traditional Japanese society still exist?

_____

_____

_____

_____

Reading Essentials and Study Guide

Chapter 16, Section 3 (continued)

• The "Asian Tigers" (page 730)

South Korea, Taiwan, Singapore, and Hong Kong have imitated Japan and have created successful industrial societies. They are called the "Asian tigers."

In 1953, Korea was exhausted from three years of war. It was divided into two parts at the 38th parallel. North of this line was the People's Republic of Korea (North Korea) under the Communist leader Kim Il Sung. South of the line was the Republic of Korea (South Korea) under the dictatorial president Syngman Rhee. In South Korea, there were several years of harsh rule and government corruption. Demonstrations broke out in the capital city of Seoul in the spring of 1960. Rhee was forced to retire. Two years later, General Chung Hee Park was elected president. He began to strengthen the economy. Land was given to the peasants, and new industries were promoted. The key industries were chemicals, textiles, and shipbuilding. In the 1980s, South Korea began to move into automobile production. But South Korea was slow to develop democratic principles. Park ruled by autocratic means and suppressed protest. Many people began to demonstrate against government policies. Democracy finally came in the 1990s. Elections held in 1997 brought the reformer Kim Tae-jung to the presidency.

In Taiwan, Chiang Kai-shek and his followers established a capital at Taipei. The government continued to call itself the Republic of China. Chiang Kai-shek's government maintained that it was the legitimate government of China and would eventually return to the mainland. Taiwan was protected by the American military. This made it possible for Taiwan to concentrate on economic growth. Taiwan made good use of foreign aid and the efforts of its own people. It was able to build a modern industrialized society. A land-reform program put farmland in the hands of peasants and doubled food production. With government help, local manufacturing and commerce expanded. Prosperity did not at first lead to democracy, however. Under Chiang Kai-shek, the government refused to allow new political parties to form. After the death of Chiang in 1975, the Republic of China slowly began to move toward a more representative form of government. By 2000, free elections had let opposition parties win control of the presidency and the legislature. Unification is still a major issue for Taiwan. The People's Republic of China on the mainland is still committed to eventual unification. The United States supports self-determination for the people of Taiwan.

Singapore was once a British colony and is now an independent state. Under the leadership of Prime Minister Lee Kuan Yew, Singapore developed an industrial economy based on shipbuilding, oil refineries, and electronics. Singapore has also become the banking center of the region. Singapore has an authoritarian political system. The prime minister once said that democracy was not appropriate for Singapore. But its citizens are beginning to demand more political freedoms.

Reading Essentials and Study Guide

Chapter 16, Section 3 (continued)

Hong Kong has also become an industrial powerhouse with high standards of living. For over 150 years, Hong Kong was under British rule. In 1997, Great Britain returned control of Hong Kong to mainland China. China promised that, for the next 50 years, Hong Kong would enjoy a high degree of economic freedom under a capitalist system. Hong Kong's future, however, remains uncertain.

9. What are the "Asian tigers"? Why are they called this?

_____

_____

_____

_____

_____

• **Australia and New Zealand** (page 733)

Both Australia and New Zealand have identified themselves culturally and politically with Europe rather than with their Asian neighbors. Their economies are <u>derived</u> from the industrialized countries of the world. Both are members of the British Commonwealth. Since the majority of the people in both Australia and New Zealand have European origins, cultural differences often hinder mutual understanding between the two countries and their Asian neighbors. However, in recent years, trends have been drawing both countries closer to Asia. Immigration from East and Southeast Asia has increased. Trade relations with Asia are also increasing. About 60 percent of Australia's export markets are now in East Asia.

Academic Vocabulary
derive: to take, receive, or obtain from a specified source (p. 733)

10. In what ways are Australia and New Zealand more like European countries than Asian countries?

_____

_____

_____

_____

_____

Reading Essentials and Study Guide

Chapter 17, Section 1

For use with textbook pages 743–748

THE CHALLENGES OF OUR WORLD

CONTENT VOCABULARY

ecology the study of the relationship between living things and their environment *(page 744)*

deforestation the clearing of forests *(page 744)*

ozone layer a thin layer of gas in the upper atmosphere that shields Earth from the Sun's ultra-violet rays *(page 745)*

greenhouse effect global warming caused by the buildup of carbon dioxide in the atmosphere *(page 745)*

acid rain the rainfall that results when sulfur produced by factories mixes with moisture in the air *(page 745)*

sustainable development economic development that does not limit the ability of future generations to meet their basic needs *(page 745)*

biowarfare the use of disease or poison against civilians and soldiers in wartime *(page 747)*

bioterrorism the use of biological and chemical weapons in terrorist attacks *(page 747)*

DRAWING FROM EXPERIENCE

Do you or your family recycle cans and other types of containers? Are there any other things that you do to help the environment?

In this section, you will read about the environmental, economic, social, and political challenges facing the world at the end of the twentieth century.

California History Social Science Standards

10.10 Students analyze instances of nation-building in the contemporary world in two of the following regions or countries: the Middle East, Africa, Mexico, and other parts of Latin America, and China.
10.11 Students analyze the integration of countries into the world economy and the information, technological, and communications revolutions (e.g., television, satellites, computers).

Reading Essentials and Study Guide

Chapter 17, Section 1 *(continued)*

Use the diagram below to help you take notes. Hunger is a huge problem in many parts of the world. List five reasons why hunger continues to be a problem.

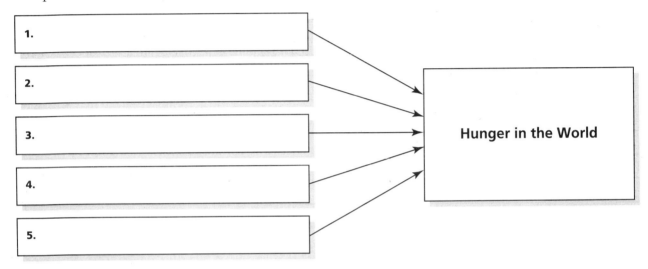

1.

2.

3.

4.

5.

Hunger in the World

- **The Environmental Crisis** *(page 744)*

In 1962, an American scientist, Rachel Carson, wrote a book called *Silent Spring*. In it she warned that the use of pesticides (chemicals sprayed on crops to kill insects) was having deadly results. The pesticides were killing birds, fish, and other wild animals. The pesticide residue on food was also harmful to human beings. Carson's warning alarmed many scientists. It led to a new field of science called **ecology** (the study of the relationship between living things and their environment). Many people became more aware of the dangers to the environment.

Dangers to the environment have many sources. A rapid increase in world population has led many people to fear that the Earth's resources simply cannot support the growing number of human beings. **Deforestation** (the clearing of forests) is one result of the growing population. Forests and jungles are cut down to provide farmland and firewood for people on Earth. As forests are cut down, dwelling places for plants and animals are destroyed. The destruction of tropical rain forests is a special concern. The tropical rain forests support 50 percent of the world's species of plants and animals. They are also crucial to human survival. They remove carbon dioxide from the air and return oxygen to it.

Reading Essentials and Study Guide

Chapter 17, Section 1 (continued)

Another danger to the environment is chemical waste. Chlorofluorocarbons are a particular concern. They are the gases used in aerosol cans, refrigerators, and air conditioners. Many scientists warn that the release of chlorofluorocarbons is destroying the **ozone layer** (a thin layer of gas in the upper atmosphere that shields Earth from the Sun's ultraviolet rays). Other scientists have proposed that there is a **greenhouse effect** (global warming caused by the buildup of carbon dioxide in the atmosphere). Another problem is **acid rain** (the rainfall that results when sulfur from factories mixes with moisture in the air). Acid rain has killed forests in both North America and Europe.

Major ecological disasters have also occurred during the last 20 years. The nuclear explosion at Chernobyl in 1986 and the oil spill caused by the oil tanker *Exxon Valdez* in 1989 are two examples. These disasters made people aware of the need to deal with environmental problems. In 1987, representatives of 43 nations met in Montreal. They agreed to protect the Earth's ozone layer by reducing the use of chlorofluorocarbons. In 1997, more than 150 nations signed the Kyoto Protocol to reduce emission.

The UN has promoted a system of **sustainable development,** economic development that does not limit the ability of future generations to meet their basic needs. One of the most basic needs of life is water. In 2003, the UN noted that one-sixth of the world's population does not have water for drinking and agriculture. The inability to get clean water leads to sickness and death. Many nations have reacted to this threat by starting recycling and water conservation programs and by controlling the dumping of toxic materials.

6. Why are the rain forests a special environmental concern?

_____

_____

_____

Reading Essentials and Study Guide

Chapter 17, Section 1 *(continued)*

- ## The Technological Revolution *(page 746)*

    Modern transportation and communication systems are transforming the world. Jumbo jets, the Internet, satellites, cable television, fax machines, and cellular telephones are some examples. The exploration of space has led to many world-changing developments. In 1969, the American astronauts Neil Armstrong and Buzz Aldrin landed on the moon. Since then, space probes have increased our understanding of distant planets. Satellites provide information about weather and transmit signals for radio, television, and telephone communications.

    In the field of health new medicines allow doctors to treat both physical and <u>mental</u> illnesses. New technologies have enabled doctors to perform "miracle" operations. Mechanical valves and pumps for the heart and organ transplants have allowed people to live longer lives. Technological changes in the health field have also raised new concerns. For example, genetic engineering is a new scientific field that alters the genetic information of cells to produce new variations. Some people worry that the new variations could be deadly. The issues of stem-cell research and human cloning have also created intense debates.

Academic Vocabulary
mental: of or relating to the total emotional and intellectual response of an individual to external reality (p. 746)

    In agriculture, the Green Revolution has promised huge returns. The Green Revolution refers to the development of new strains of rice, corn, and other grains that have greater yields. It was promoted as the technological solution to feeding the world's growing population. But immense amounts of chemical fertilizers and pesticides are needed to grow the new strains. Many farmers cannot afford the fertilizers, and the pesticides create environmental problems.

    The technological revolution has also led to the development of <u>nuclear</u>, biological, and chemical weapons. Although the end of the Cold War reduced the chances of a major nuclear war, there is still concern that nuclear materials (bombs or radioactive matter) will be obtained and used by terrorists. **Biowarfare** (the use of disease and poison against civilians and soldiers in wartime) is not new. Chemical weapons were used extensively in World War I and in the Iran-Iraq War in the 1980s. Governments have made agreements to limit the research, production, and use of biological and chemical weapons. But these agreements have not prevented terrorists from practicing **bioterrorism** (the use of biological and chemical weapons in terrorist attacks).

Academic Vocabulary
nuclear: of or relating to the atomic nucleus (p. 745)

   7. What concerns have been raised by technological changes in the health field?

   _____

   _____

   _____

   _____

Reading Essentials and Study Guide

Chapter 17, Section 1 *(continued)*

• Political and Economic Challenges *(page 747)*

Since World War II, the world has developed a global economy (an economy in which the production, distribution, and sale of goods take place on a worldwide scale). In 1995, the World Trade Organization (WTO) was established. Trade agreements are negotiated, signed, and upheld by its member nations. The WTO has been criticized for placing commercial interests above environmental and health concerns and for favoring the wealthier countries.

One of the features of the global economy is the wide gap between rich, or industrialized, nations and poor, or developing, nations. The rich nations are mainly in the Northern Hemisphere. They have well-organized industrial and agricultural systems, advanced technologies, and strong educational systems. The poor nations are located mainly in Africa, Asia, and Latin America. They are primarily farming nations with little technology. A serious problem in developing countries is rapid population growth. Much of the growth is occurring in poor countries that can least afford it.

Hunger has also become a staggering problem that kills over 8 million people every year. Rapid population growth, poor soil, natural catastrophes, and economic and political factors contribute to widespread hunger. For example, during Sudan's civil war in the 1980s, neither side would allow food to be sent to their enemy. As a result, 1.3 million people starved.

Within a decade of World War II, military dictatorships or one-party governments had replaced democratic systems in many developing countries. Many leaders underestimated the difficulty of building democratic political systems. Recently, there have been signs of renewed interest in democracy in various parts of the world.

Regional, ethnic, and religious differences continue to create conflict around the world. In Europe, Yugoslavia has been torn apart by ethnic divisions. In the Middle East, the conflict between Israelis and Palestinians continues to produce acts of violence. Conflicts between ethnic groups in Africa have led to massacres of hundreds of thousands of people.

8. What differences continue to create conflicts around the world?

_____

_____

_____

_____

_____

Reading Essentials and Study Guide

Chapter 17, Section 2

For use with textbook pages 749–753

GLOBAL VISIONS

CONTENT VOCABULARY

peacekeeping force a military force drawn from neutral members of the United Nations to settle conflicts and supervise truces *(page 751)*

disarmament groups organizations working toward limiting or reducing armed forces and weapons *(page 752)*

DRAWING FROM EXPERIENCE

Have you heard the slogan "Think globally, act locally"? What do you think this slogan means? How might this slogan be carried out in your community?

In the last section, you read about global challenges faced in recent decades. In this section, you will read about international organizations formed to respond to these challenges. You will also read about groups led by ordinary citizens that have tried to address some of these problems.

ORGANIZING YOUR THOUGHTS

Use the chart below to help you take notes. The United Nations is one of the organizations that have tried to address global problems. List the three main parts of the United Nations and describe their functions. Also list three of the specialized agencies that are under the direction of the United Nations.

California History Social Science Standards

10.9 Students analyze the international developments in the post-World War II world.
10.10 Students analyze instances of nation-building in the contemporary world in two of the following regions or countries: the Middle East, Africa, Mexico, and other parts of Latin America, and China.

Focuses on:
10.9.8, 10.10.2, 10.10.3

United Nations		
1.	**2.**	**3.**

4.	**5.**	**6.**

Glencoe World History—Modern Times

Reading Essentials and Study Guide

Chapter 17, Section 2 *(continued)*

READ TO LEARN

- ## The United Nations *(page 750)*

Representatives of the Allied forces founded the United Nations (UN) in 1945. The United Nations had two main goals: peace and human dignity and welfare. The General Assembly of the United Nations is made up of representatives of all member nations. It has the power to discuss any question of importance to the organization and to recommend the action to be taken. The most important advisory group of the UN is the Security Council. It is made up of 5 permanent members (the United States, Russia, Great Britain, France, and China) and 10 members chosen by the General Assembly to serve limited terms. The Security Council decides what actions the UN should take to settle international disputes. The administration of the UN is directed by the secretary-general from the central offices in New York City.

Several specialized agencies function under the direction of the United Nations. These include the United Nations Educational, Scientific, and Cultural Organization (UNESCO), the World Health Organization (WHO), and the United Nations International Children's Emergency Fund (UNICEF). All of these agencies have been successful in helping to address economic and social problems. The United Nations has also organized international conferences on important issues such as population growth and the environment. It has also provided **peacekeeping forces** (military forces drawn from neutral member states to settle conflicts and supervise truces) on various occasions.

7. What are the two main goals of the United Nations?

_____

_____

_____

_____

_____

- ## New Global Visions *(page 752)*

One <u>approach</u> to global problems has been the development of social movements led by ordinary citizens. These movements have addressed issues such as environmental problems, women's liberation, human potential, technology, and nonviolence. "Think globally, act locally" is the slogan of such groups.

Academic Vocabulary
approach: to take preliminary steps toward a particular purpose (p. 752)

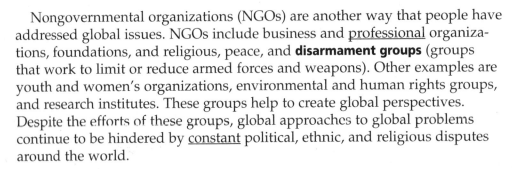

Nongovernmental organizations (NGOs) are another way that people have addressed global issues. NGOs include business and <u>professional</u> organizations, foundations, and religious, peace, and **disarmament groups** (groups that work to limit or reduce armed forces and weapons). Other examples are youth and women's organizations, environmental and human rights groups, and research institutes. These groups help to create global perspectives. Despite the efforts of these groups, global approaches to global problems continue to be hindered by <u>constant</u> political, ethnic, and religious disputes around the world.

Academic Vocabulary
professional: of, relating to, or characteristic of a profession (p. 752)

Academic Vocabulary
constant: continually occurring or recurring (p. 753)

8. What are NGOs? What are some examples?

_____

_____

_____

_____

_____